Poetry skills

Learning language through poetry

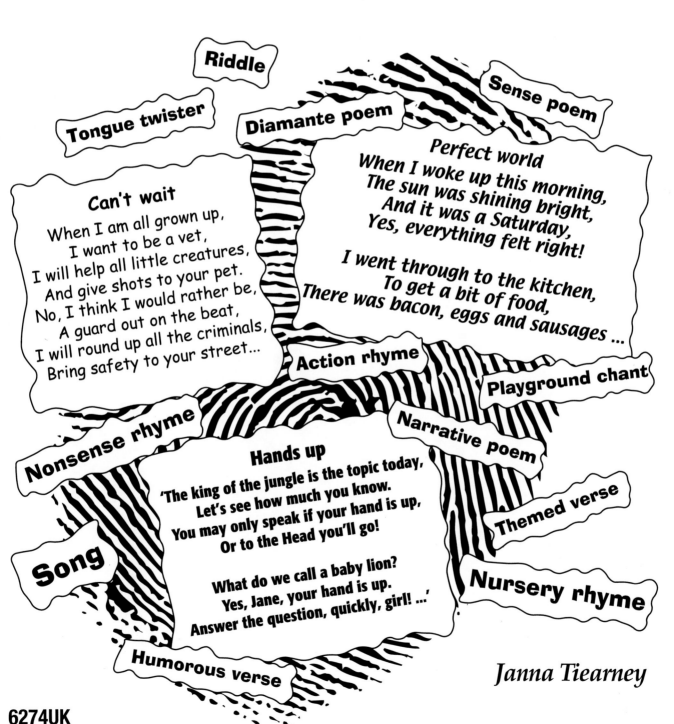

Riddle

Tongue twister

Diamante poem

Sense poem

Perfect world
When I woke up this morning,
The sun was shining bright,
And it was a Saturday,
Yes, everything felt right!

I went through to the kitchen,
To get a bit of food,
There was bacon, eggs and sausages ...

Can't wait
When I am all grown up,
I want to be a vet,
I will help all little creatures,
And give shots to your pet.
No, I think I would rather be,
A guard out on the beat,
I will round up all the criminals,
Bring safety to your street...

Action rhyme

Playground chant

Nonsense rhyme

Narrative poem

Themed verse

Hands up
'The king of the jungle is the topic today,
Let's see how much you know.
You may only speak if your hand is up,
Or to the Head you'll go!

What do we call a baby lion?
Yes, Jane, your hand is up.
Answer the question, quickly, girl! ...'

Song

Nursery rhyme

Humorous verse

Janna Tiearney

6274UK
75/7

POETRY SKILLS *(Lower)*

Published by Prim-Ed Publishing® 2007
Copyright© Janna Tiearney 2006
ISBN-978 1 84654 063 9
PR–6274

Additional titles available in this series:

POETRY SKILLS *(Middle)*

POETRY SKILLS *(Upper)*

Internet websites

In some cases, websites or specific URLs may be recommended. While these are checked and rechecked at the time of publication, the publisher has no control over any subsequent changes which may be made to webpages. It is *strongly* recommended that the class teacher checks *all* URLs before allowing pupils to access them.

View all pages online

Website: www.prim-ed.com

Email: sales@prim-ed.com

Foreword

Poetry skills is a fun and innovative series, designed to help pupils learn and practise the English language. It is not a series purely to teach poetry, but rather a means to study language through the medium of poetry.

With the ever-increasing burden placed on them, teachers will find these lessons practical and enjoyable, with structured lessons to include all key areas of the curriculum, and to develop all the necessary skills.

Poetry is a child-friendly way to approach the teaching of language through reading, and listening to and writing poetry, which will not only benefit the pupil's language awareness but also increase his/her confidence.

There is a selection of humorous and relevant poems on familiar topics. Many different types of poems have been included, which will give pupils the opportunity to experience and explore different types of text and settings. Pupils enjoy poems with rhythm and rhyme and many of the included poems contain these elements.

Since poetry requires a certain amount of fluency, pupils' reading skills will be developed, in a more exciting and interesting way, through reading, practising, reciting and learning poetry. Comprehension skills will also be enhanced.

The shorter texts and flexibility of lessons make this book suitable for both mainstream and special needs pupils.

The shorter written tasks will prove less daunting and will enable pupils to complete work in which all their learned skills will be utilised.

Through studying poetry, pupils will be given the chance to explore feelings—their own and the feelings of others—and will in turn, be able to express their own feelings on a range of subjects, while drawing on their own personal experiences and their imagination.

> ***A poem is not a thing we see, but rather a light by which we may see ... and what we see is life.***
>
> ***Robert Penn Warren***

The books in this series are:

Poetry skills – Lower (5–7 years)

Poetry skills – Middle (7–9 years)

Poetry skills – Upper (9–11+ years)

Curriculum links

Country	Subject	Level	Objectives
England	Literacy	Year 1	• Read aloud with some pace and emphasis. • Listen with sustained concentration. • Recognise the main elements that shape different texts. • Explore the effects of patterns of language and repeated words and phrases. • Comment on texts, making imaginative links to their own experiences. • Choose and plan writing.
		Year 2	• Use appropriate intonation when reading and reciting texts. • Present drama to members of their own class. • Draw together ideas from across a whole text. • Explain their reactions to texts. • Draw on knowledge and experience of texts in deciding what and how to write. • Make adventurous word and language choices appropriate to the style of the text.
Northern Ireland	Language and literacy	KS 1	• Listen to, respond to and explore poems and recreate parts of them in drama. • Take part in drama activities. • Express thoughts, feelings and opinions in response to literature. • Read aloud. • Discuss features of language; e.g. rhyming words. • Use appropriate quality of speech and voice, speaking audibly and clearly. • Engage with a range of poems. • Read and be read to from a wide selection of poetry. • Take part in shared and paired reading experiences. • Retell, re-read and act out familiar poems. • Compose, read and share poems. • Begin to use evidence from text to support their views. • Write creatively using a variety of forms; e.g. poems. • Experiment with words; e.g. riddles and rhymes. • Use imagination to express thoughts and feelings in written form. • Experiment with simple poetic forms.
Scotland	English	Level B	• Listen to texts with more demanding language and structure. • Listen to poems with simple imagery. • Listen to poems with different distinguishing features; e.g. rhyme, rhythm. • Explore experiences from poems. • Reflect on poems through drawing, mime and role-play. • Justify poetry preferences. • Experience different styles of poetry. • Read aloud and share texts they have enjoyed. • Use a model and vocabulary suggestions to aid writing. • Discuss structures and effects of poems read before writing, especially rhythm and vocabulary.
Wales	English	KS 1	• Read and listen to nursery rhymes and poetry. • Read aloud. • Work in groups and present work to different audiences. • Participate in drama activities. • Read on their own and with others from a range of genres. • Experience language with recognisable repetitive patterns, rhyme and rhythm. • Read poems with familiar and imaginary settings. • Read poems and chants containing patterned and predictable language. • Understand and respond to poems. • Hear poems read aloud. • Prepare, present and act out poems. • Write poems in response to a variety of stimuli. • Write in a range of forms; e.g. poems. • Organise imaginative writing in different ways.

Contents

Teachers notes

Teachers page

A teachers page accompanies each pupil worksheet. It provides the following information:

Objective/Activities covered

The activity objective and a list of activities are included for easy reference.

Background information for each activity is included for the teacher.

Learning about lions
Teachers notes

Objective
Find information and shares it with others

Activities covered
- Reading a poem
- Completing research about lions
- Writing five facts
- Sharing information with a group

Background information
For this lesson, pupils must be given time to research the information. The lesson is about sharing their information with their group. Pupils must be told to listen quietly and patiently while others are speaking. The topic should not be discussed before the groups get together. A class discussion should only occur once all pupils have contributed to the group's discussion.

Before the lesson
The teacher should collate a list of facts about lions to discuss with the class once the lesson is over.
Pupils will need access to information about lions.
Pupils will need to research to complete this lesson. This may be in the form of a homework activity or could be completed in class.
The pupils will be divided into groups.

The lesson
1. The teacher reads the poem **Hands up** with the class. The topic of lions is not discussed at this point, nor the correct answers to the questions in the poem. As the poem introduces the topic, it may be necessary for the teacher to read it twice.
2. Pupils are given time to research the topic. This could occur before this lesson.
3. Pupils discuss in groups the five facts they learnt about lions. Pupils then attempt to answer the questions in the poem correctly.
4. Pupils write one new fact they learnt from their group. (If no new facts, they can write one after the class discussion.)
5. The topic is discussed as a class.

Answers
1. Teacher check
2. Facts about lions:
   - Very sociable creatures, live in groups called prides
   - They are carnivores
   - Have excellent sight, hearing and sense of smell
   - When a lion is about to charge, it lashes its tail up and down, flattens its ears and simultaneously roars
   - Both males and females roar as a means of communication
   - Usually silent when hunting
   - Vocal calls range from a loud roar to a low, soft, moaning cough
   - Very powerful animals
   - Good jumpers and swimmers
   - Powerful claws are fully retractable
   - Females are the principal killers
   - At the top of the food chain, no natural enemies, biggest enemy is people
   - Hunt mainly at night
3. The correct answers to questions in the poem are: baby lion – cub, lions eat meat, a group is called a pride, biggest enemy is man
4. Teacher check

Additional activities
Pupils can:
1. Ask their family how life was different when they were the pupils' age, for homework, and then share this information with the group.
2. Complete a group project with each pupil contributing something.

Recommended reading:
The Lion by Roald Dahl

Website:
<www.nationalgeographic.com/kids/creature_feature/0109/lions2.html>

Before the lesson – the teacher is made aware of what needs to be done before the lesson. Some materials and tasks are required for the lesson to be conducted; others are suggestions that will enrich the lesson.

The lesson – gives suggested step-by-step instructions for using the worksheet. Often, a list of words contained in a poem that may require clarification is included, as it is important that all words in a poem are understood by the pupils.

Answers – for the activities are included. Some answers will need a teacher check, while others may vary depending on personal experiences, opinions or feelings.

Additional activities – can be used to further develop the objective of the worksheet. These activities provide ideas to consolidate and clarify the concepts and skills taught in the lesson.

Recommended reading – provides further examples of the type of poetry being studied. Poetry books should be available in the classroom and school library for the pupils to access. It is important for pupils to read, and have read to them, poetry by different authors, as the poems on the worksheets have all been written by the same author.

Websites – are suggested on many pages to help teachers and/or pupils find other examples of poetry. Websites were current and appropriate at the time of printing; however, teachers should check before allowing the pupils to use them, and refer to their school's Internet policy.

Teachers notes

Pupil page

Poem

A poem, usually on a familiar topic, is found on each pupil page. Many different types of poems have been included to give the pupils the opportunity to experience and explore a variety of text and settings and to motivate them. Poetry forms used include concrete poetry, haiku, cinquain, list, clerihew, sense, sausage, chant and tongue twister. Pupils enjoy rhyming poems with humour and a strong rhythm, and many of the poems in this book contain these elements. The importance of rhyme and rhythm could be emphasised by having the pupils beat out their rhythm by clapping or using musical instruments.

- Through the lesson, the pupils will learn that poetry comes in a variety of forms, but always expresses important personal feelings and gives a unique insight into the mind of the creator.

- If the poem is to be read aloud, the teacher should use much expression to promote enthusiasm, as some pupils have a negative view of poetry.

Activities

- In the activities, the pupils will be given the chance to explore and express feelings (their own and those of others) on a range of subjects, while drawing on their own experiences and imagination.

- The activity may:
  - introduce or reinforce a topic
  - allow for expression of thoughts, feelings and moods
  - allow for discussion of personal opinions and interpretations of a poem
  - promote a love of words.

- Discussion is a vital part of lessons and may include class, group or pair work. This will give the pupils the opportunity to share their efforts and experiences.

- Pupils are encouraged on many of the worksheets to check or self-assess their work.

- Interesting facts, jokes or common sayings have been included on many of the worksheets. Teachers could use these as a springboard for further discussion or writing tasks.

Further ideas

- It is suggested that the pupils keep a 'Poetry portfolio'. This will allow the teacher to quickly see what worksheets have been covered.

- The pupils' poetry efforts should be praised and their work displayed on a regular basis in the classroom, around the school, in the school newspaper or in a class anthology. This should occur in an atmosphere where criticism is both positive and constructive, encouraging the pupils to be innovative and to take risks with their writing.

Objective
Listen to a poem and respond to it

Activities covered
- Reading a poem as a class
- Discussing as a class
- Writing ideas
- Summing up ideas

Background information
Pupils need to be given the opportunity to respond to things they hear in a variety of ways as opposed to listening passively. They should be encouraged to ask questions and to participate in discussion.

Recommended reading:
(poems for pupils to respond to)

Said the boy to the dinosaur
by Colin McNaughton

Blue Christmas by Adrian Henri

The rival arrives by Brian Patten

Website:
(stories for the teacher to read)
<www.kidinfo.com/Young_children/Young_Children.html >

Before the lesson
Other poems can be read to the pupils.

The lesson
1. Read the poem **Weekends** as a class.
2. The pupils circle things they might do on a weekend.
3. Hold a class discussion about how the poet's weekend is similar to or different from the pupils' usual weekends.
4. The pupils discuss what they could do to prevent boredom on weekends, then list their favourite ideas.
5. The pupils sum up their usual weekend in one word.

Answers
1.–2. Teacher check
3. Some ideas: read, take the dog for walk, help with family chores such as cooking, tidy room, take up a hobby like painting, visit someone, write letters to friends, take photos, make a vegetable patch, take up a sport.
4.–5. Teacher check

Additional activities
Pupils can:
1. Listen to stories and orally change aspects of them.
2. Listen to/watch adverts and decide which information is truthful and which might be exaggerated.
3. Look at the school rules and discuss which are fair or unfair. Formulate their own set of classroom rules.

1 As a class, read the following poem.

I'm ready for my weekend!

> ### Weekends
>
> *In the morning getting snug*
> *drinking coffee from a mug.*
>
> *Watching TV in the day*
> *having breakfast on a tray.*
>
> *Playing with friends you really like*
> *talking a lot, riding your bike.*
>
> *Having takeaways for your tea*
> *without homework feeling free.*
>
> *Weekends are the very best*
> *to play, to laugh, to run, to rest.*

2 Circle the things in the poem you usually do on weekends.

3 (a) Discuss some things you could do if you felt bored on the weekends.

(b) Write a list of the ideas you liked the most.

_____

_____

4 Would you enjoy the poet's weekend?   ☐ Yes ☐ No

Say why/why not. _____

_____

_____

5 Sum up your usual weekend in one word: [_____]

Quiet please!

Objective

Listen to sounds and respond to them

Activities covered

- Reading sound poem as a group
- Underlining sound words
- Reading poem and adding sound effects
- Assessing performance
- Writing what ideas come to mind from hearing different sounds

Background information

During the lesson, the class can discuss sounds heard in different places; e.g. at school, at home, in the environment, in a busy street, at an airport, in a bowling alley. Consider natural sounds and sounds made by machines. Practising outside would be best if the weather permits.

Recommended reading:

'Quack!' said the billy goat
by Charles Causley
Innocent by Steve Turner (onomatopoeia)

Website:

(musical games)
<www.kidsdomain.com/games/music.html>

Before the lesson

The class should be divided into small groups.
Examples of other sounds could be provided.

The lesson

1. Discuss examples of different sounds with the pupils. The class can then sit quietly for a minute to listen to the sounds around them before discussing them.
2. In small groups, read the poem **Keep quiet!**, with each member of each group reading a line.
3. The pupils underline the sound words in the poem.
4. Each group decides how it will make the sounds in the poem. The pupils then read the poem. (If possible, groups should practise outside so that they can't see or hear what other groups are doing.)
5. The pupils perform their poems for the class, then assess their performance by colouring a face.
6. The pupils write what the sound words make them think of, starting each sentence with 'I think of ...'.

Answers

1. Teacher check
2. squeak, knocking, burps, laughing, boom, squeal, crash, sneezing, splashes, banging
3.–5. Teacher check

Additional activities

Pupils can:

1. Listen to wildlife sounds on a CD.
2. Listen to a recording of themselves in class.
3. Think of sound words associated with a particular topic; e.g. 'The shopping centre'.
4. Write sound poems.
5. Make up sound words.

Homework suggestion

Write all the sounds heard at home, and report back to the class.

1 In a small group, read the following poem. Each person should take turns to say a line. Keep going until the poem is finished.

> Sound travels at about 760 miles an hour.

Keep quiet!

The squeak of Bev's chair on the floor,
Ryan is knocking on the classroom door,
Michael burps, he's no manners at all,
James is laughing with Ann in the hall,
The boom of Mary's voice all day,
The squeal of Thomas out at play,
Oh, oops, the crash of breaking glass,
Brian keeps sneezing during class,
Louise splashes water and paint around,
The school band makes a banging sound,
The school is never free of noise,
Because it's filled with girls and boys!

2 Underline the sound words.

3 In your group, decide how to make the sounds in the poem. Practise reading the poem with your sound effects. Perform your poem for the class.

4 Colour a face to show how well you performed your poem.

5 As a group, write what these sound words make you think of.

(a) bang!   I think of _____

(b) creak!   _____

(c) ping!   _____

(d) whoosh!   _____

(e) squeak!   _____

(f) pop!   _____

(g) boom!   _____

And ... action!

Objective

Use gesture and movement to extend the meaning of what he/she is saying

Activities covered

- Reading as a class
- Identifying actions as a group
- Reading a poem and adding actions
- Performing a poem
- Assessing performance of a poem
- Making a list

Background information

We use nonverbal communication every day to communicate feelings, ideas and information. We may use gestures, body language or other movements on their own, but may also use them to add to what we are saying; e.g. pointing to show directions or how big something was.

Recommended reading:

(for adding actions)
The itch by Michael Rosen

Website:

(for teacher)
<www.songsforteaching.com/
autisticchildren/bodytalklanguage.htm>

Before the lesson

The teacher should have a list of examples of how we use gesture and movement in our everyday lives.

The class should be divided into small groups.

The lesson

1. Discuss with the pupils common everyday gestures that we use; e.g. goodbye, hello, please, go away, I don't know, I'm angry, I'm sad, I'm tired. The pupils demonstrate for the class.
2. Read the poem ***Late again*** as a class.
3. Discuss any difficult words, such as 'horrid', 'chores', 'porridge'.
4. In small groups, the pupils circle all the action words in the poem.
5. As a group, the pupils add actions to the poem and practise it. This could be done outside if the weather permits, so that the groups do not see or hear what the others are doing.
6. The groups perform their poems for the class and assess their performance.
7. The pupils make a list of things they have to do in the mornings.

Answers

1.–6. Teacher check

Additional activities

Pupils can:

1. Tell the class something by using movement and gesture only.
2. Pretend to be an animal using movement only. The class must guess what animal each pupil is miming.
3. In groups, act out a short play using no words at all.
4. Watch an old silent film. Discuss how the story was told without spoken words.

Homework suggestion

Use gesture and movement to tell a family member about their day at school.

And ... action!

Sometimes we use actions when we speak; for example,
waving when we say goodbye.

Late again

I hate the weekday mornings,
There's far too much to do!
I have to put on my uniform,
And look for my other shoe.
I have to brush my knotty hair,
I have to wash my face,
Mum screams at me to 'HURRY UP!'
You'd swear it was a race.
I have to eat my porridge,
And drink a cup of tea,
Gobble a pot of yoghurt,
And take my Vitamin C.
I have to pack my schoolbag,
And check my homework's done,
Tidy my entire room,
There is no time for fun!
I have to feed the starving cat,
Who meows and will not wait,
With all these horrid chores to do,
It's no wonder I am late!

1 Read this poem together as a class.

2 In small groups, circle all the action words in the poem.

3 In your groups, read the poem together and add actions. List some actions below.

_____

_____

_____

_____

4 Practise your poem, then perform it for the class.

5 Give your performance a score out of 5 (5 is the best).

6 List some things you usually do in the morning.

I usually _____

_____

Objective

Practise reading a poem to improve performance

Activities covered

- Listening to the teacher read poetry
- Reading a poem, taking note of mistakes
- Reading a poem to a partner
- Giving a partner a score for reading aloud
- Improving a poem reading

Background information

Pupils learn from example; therefore, it is important that they hear the teacher reading often, using expression, clarity and correct pronunciation. The teacher can write on the board/have displayed in the classroom what to be aware of when reading.

For example:

- Pronounce words correctly (Say words properly)
- Use expression
- Speak clearly

Before the lesson

Other poems could be read to the pupils.

The class should be divided into pairs.

The lesson

1. Read aloud the poem *Good news?* to the pupils.
2. Explain to the pupils what the lesson is about and what will happen next. Difficult words from the poem can be explained, such as 'uniform', 'laundry', 'starving', 'pounding'.
3. Have the pupils practise reading the poem quietly to themselves. They can then mark any parts of the poem they are finding difficult to read. This will make them more careful in these areas.
4. Pupils read the poem to their partner and give each other a score out of 5. Encourage the pupils to be fair.
5. The pupils list ways they could improve their reading, and then indicate whether they feel they improved after a second reading.

Answers

1.–6. Teacher check

Additional activities

Pupils can:

1. Listen to the teacher read aloud a range of texts; e.g. other poetry, interesting newspaper articles, sections of the class reader, jokes, short stories (which are great for that rare moment where there are a few minutes spare).
2. Listen to stories on a CD.
3. Listen to others read in group situations.

Homework suggestion

Read *Good news?* to a family member.

Recommended reading:

Teacher's prayer by Allan Ahlberg

Where do all the teachers go? by Peter Dixon

The excuse by Jane Wright

The dragon by Barry Buckingham

Websites:

(poetry for the teacher to read)

<www.gigglepoetry.com>

<www.poetry4kids.com>

<www.shadowpoetry.com>

Good news?

Oh no! I am very, very late,
I should be at school!
My alarm clock must be broken!
I will look like such a fool!

I have to get ready really quick!
Where is my uniform?
It must be in the laundry bin!
It's dirty and it's worn!

I am starving! Let me grab some food,
Oh crumpets, there is no bread!
I cannot seem to find my shoes!
I have a pounding head!

Oh, everything is going wrong!
It will be a bad, bad day!
Then Mum says, 'You're up early,
On this sunny Saturday!'

1 Listen to this poem.

2 Practise reading the poem quietly to yourself.

3 Mark the difficult parts of the poem so you know where to be careful.

4 Read the poem to a partner. Ask your partner to give you a score out of 5 (5 is the best).

5 Write your score. ☐

6 (a) Try to improve on your score. List some ways you could do this.

_____

_____

_____

_____

(b) Read your poem again.

| Use expression when you are reading! |

Did you feel you improved?

☐ Yes   ☐ No

What score would you give yourself now? ☐

Objective

Engage in shared reading activities

Activities covered

- Reading a poem as a group
- Making a poem sound more interesting
- Performing a poem for the class
- Assessing a performance
- Drawing ideas

Background information

Reading can be a sociable activity. Reading in groups may be less intimidating for shy pupils and provides an opportunity for pupils to help each other out and share their thoughts and feelings. In this lesson, the pupils are making a poem sound interesting and therefore different roles will need to be assigned by the pupils themselves.

Recommended reading:

The ghost teacher by Allan Ahlberg

I'm much better than you by Colin McNaughton

Secret by Elizabeth Carr (for pairs)

Whispers of love by Janis Preistley

Before the lesson

The class should be divided into small groups.

The lesson

1. Read the poem **Sunshine** as a class.
2. In small groups, the pupils read the poem together.
3. As a group, the pupils decide how they will perform the poem for the class.
4. The groups have some time to practise the poem and then perform it for the class and assess their performance.
5. As a group, the topic of sunshine is discussed. The pupils can draw their ideas. Some may like to share their ideas with the class.

Answers

1.–4. Teacher check

Additional activities

Pupils can:

1. Practise shared reading in other subjects, such as history or geography.
2. Complete comprehension exercises in small groups.
3. In small groups, have a short story to read, with each member of the group taking a turn to read.
4. In pairs or groups, follow instructions, to make something; e.g. an origami animal.
5. Read plays in groups.

Homework suggestion

Read a given poem with a family member.

Sunshine

Rain had fallen for days and days,
and then the sun came through.
Dad said, 'Go and get the steak,
we'll have a barbecue'.

Mum said, 'Great, I'll hang out the clothes,
I'll have dry washing at last'.
Josh said, 'I'm going to ride my bike,
watch me go right past'.

Jason said, 'I'll be skateboarding,
I can practise my new trick'.
'I'm off to visit a friend', said James,
'Being indoors makes me sick!'

The cat said,' I'm off to frighten birds,
don't wait up for me'.
I went outside to soak up the heat,
the warmth was healing me.

Yes, what an enormous difference
the sun made to our day.
The house it fell quite silent,
as we all went out to play.

❶ Read this poem together as a small group.

❷ Decide as a group how you could make the poem sound more interesting by making some words louder, using character voices etc. Write on the poem who will say what, and which lines you will say together.

❸ (a) Practise reading the poem as a group. When you are ready, perform your poem for the class.

Use expression!

(b) Colour a box to show how well you feel you did.

A	=	Excellent

B	=	Good

C	=	Fair

❹ Discuss as a group how sunshine makes a difference to your day. Draw one idea below.

Sunshine gives you Vitamin D!

Objective

Continue to build a sight vocabulary of common words from poems

Activities covered

- Reading a poem
- Reading to a partner
- Ticking sentences that make sense

Background information

The pupils should have a word book in which they write all new vocabulary. These new words can then be referred to when the pupils are carrying out writing tasks. New words could also be displayed in the classroom, and the pupils should be encouraged to use them, not only in their writing, but also in their conversation. Teachers should go back to new words every now and then to make sure the pupils have remembered them.

Recommended reading:

The teacher can use sight reading passages containing words the pupils should know. Dr Seuss's *Green eggs and ham* is a good one to start with.

Before the lesson

The class should be divided into pairs.

The lesson

1. Read the poem *Heavy morning* and discuss it as a class, explaining difficult words such as 'awake', 'duvet', 'forced', 'alert', 'weight', 'blanket', 'laziness', 'nonsense' and 'squashed'.

2. The pupils take turns to read the list to their partners. They should try to read the list without stopping. Pupils tick the word when they get it right. (The pupils can read the lists a few times to each other until they get it right.)

3. The pupils tick those sentences which make sense for Question 3. In pairs, the pupils can then make sense of the nonsense sentences by using words from their reading list. This can be done orally.

4. Any new words the pupils have encountered during this activity can be written in their word books.

Answers

1.–2. Teacher check

3. (i) no (I had a bad dream last night.)
   (ii) yes
   (iii) no (I know I am pretty.)
   (iv) no (The teacher will scream at me.)
   (v) no (What is the time?)

Additional activities

Pupils can:

1. Write sentences using a given list of words.

2. Write new words and draw pictures to go with them. Display in the classroom.

3. In pairs, read other lists of words to each other.

Homework suggestion

Read the poem or a passage containing sight vocabulary to a family member.

Wake up!

Most people wake up six times a night!

Heavy morning

The alarm clock's gone off,
It's time to awake!
But the duvet's too heavy,
My bones it will break!
I can hear the whole family,
Have started their day,
Do they know that I'm trapped,
And forced here to stay?
I try to alert them,
And give a loud scream,
The weight crushes my insides,
Is this all a bad dream?
Mum rushes in and says,
'What's wrong with you?'
'I'm stuck under the blanket,
Mum, help me! Please do!'
'I am tired of your nonsense!
I will have no more!'
And I was left there to be squashed,
As she walked out the door.

❶ Read the poem and discuss the unknown words.

❷ In pairs, read these words to each other without stopping!

clock	*started*	*scream*	*blanket*
gone	*family*	*this*	*please*
time	*they*	*dream*	*help*
too	*know*	*says*	*walked*
heavy	*stay*	*wrong*	*more*
bones	*try*	*you*	
break	*give*	*stuck*	

Tick them when you get them right!

❸ (a) Do these sentences make sense? Tick YES or NO.

(b) Write a word from the list for each incorrect sentence.

(i) I had a bad wrong last night. _____ ☐ Yes ☐ No

(ii) My family is great! _____ ☐ Yes ☐ No

(iii) I clock I am pretty. _____ ☐ Yes ☐ No

(iv) The teacher will please at me. _____ ☐ Yes ☐ No

(v) What is the walked? _____ ☐ Yes ☐ No

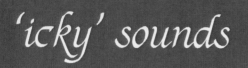
'icky' sounds

Objective

Engage in activities designed to increase awareness of sounds

Activities covered

- Finding sounds in a poem
- Choosing correct words to complete sentences
- Writing words with given sounds
- Choosing correct sounds to complete words

Background information

This type of lesson can be done with any of the sounds associated with letters and letter clusters. The pupils need to develop an awareness of sounds; therefore, the lesson should contain some discussion, so the pupils can see and hear the sound.

Before the lesson

Examples of other sounds could be explored orally.

The lesson

1. Hold a class discussion on different sounds and give examples of each.
2. The pupils find all the **'ick'** sounds in the poem.
3. The pupils choose **'ick'** words from a box to complete the sentences.
4. The pupils write words that have the given sounds in them.
5. The pupils choose the correct sound for the given words.

Answers

1. trick, stick, lick, sick
2. (a) chick (b) lick (c) thick (d) tick
3. Answers may include: wick, quick, brick, click, flick, pick
4. Answers may include the following:

   ack – back, black, hack, Jack, lack, knack, pack, quack, rack, sack, whack, shack, track, snack, crack etc.

   ock – block, dock, lock, mock, knock, rock, sock, shock, chock, clock, flock etc.

   eck – deck, fleck, neck, peck, wreck, check etc.
5. (a) sick (b) check (c) crack

Additional activities

Pupils can:

1. Play games where small groups are given a sound and asked to write words containing that sound. The group with the most words gets the most points.
2. Read class readers and pick out different sounds.
3. Write sentences or a story using as many words as possible with the same sound.
4. Write poems using a rhyming scheme.
5. Write a list of words with given sounds associated with particular topics.

All words are made up of sounds.

1 Find all the **ick** words. Write them in the box.

> *My dog can do an amazing trick,*
> *But not with a ball or stick.*
> *His nostrils he can lick -*
> *It makes me feel so sick!*

ick words

2 Choose a word from the box to finish these sentences.

(a) The hen chased after her _____.

(b) Did you _____ my ice-cream?

(c) That book is really _____.

(d) I wish the teacher would _____ my sums!

thick

chick

tick

lick

3 Write some more ick words below.

_____

4 Write words with these sounds.

ack	ock	eck

5 Choose the correct sound to complete each word.

ick	ack	eck

(a) I feel s _____ today.

(b) Please ch _____ my homework.

(c) You made that mirror cr _____.

Never trick the teacher!

Which part rhymes?

Objective

Learn about the sounds associated with the part of a word or syllable that allows it to rhyme with another word or syllable

Activities covered

- Identifying parts of words that rhyme
- Reading a poem, looking at rhyming words
- Writing rhyming words

Background information

Most pupils enjoy rhyming words, and this lesson focuses on which part of a word rhymes with another. At the beginning of the lesson, the teacher should get many examples of rhyming words from the pupils before they focus on the part of the word that rhymes; e.g. the teacher can ask 'What rhymes with "deep"?' Many examples can be written on the board. For this lesson, all rhyming words have the same letter formations as it would be too confusing to discuss words such as done/bun etc. Pupils should be aware, however, that not all rhyming words have the same letter patterns, and this can be illustrated; e.g. blue/flew.

Before the lesson

Prepare a list of rhyming words as examples.

The pupils should have colouring pencils.

The lesson

1. Ask the pupils to suggest words that rhyme. Some of these can be written on the board. (Make sure those on the board have the same letter formations; for the oral work it doesn't matter.) Show on the board the parts of the words that rhyme.
2. Discuss more difficult words such as: 'row', 'pail', 'slope'.
3. The pupils circle the parts of the words that rhyme for Question 1.
4. Read aloud the poem **Jack vs Jill** while the pupils follow.
5. Read Question 3 to the pupils to make sure that they understand what has to be done.
6. The pupils underline the words that rhyme in the poem in the same colour, and then circle the parts of the words that rhyme.
7. The pupils write three rhyming words for each of the given sounds in Question 4.

Answers

1. (a) 'ock' (b) 'ap' (c) 'oon' (d) 'able'
2. Teacher check
3. row/now, mad/lad, back/Jack, Jill/hill, cry/dry, tart/apart
4. Answers may include the following:

   ack – black, snack, track, crack, lack, pack, quack, rack, stack

   ate – rate, crate, date, fate, gate, hate, late, mate, slate

   ight – fight, night, fright, sight, tight, right, bright, height, light, might, plight

Additional activities

Pupils can:

1. Make up nonsense words from given letter sounds; e.g. 'ick' – plick, bick, yick, zick.
2. Read the poem as a class, then read aloud a list of words in the poem. The pupils must find them and colour them in, or colour in words that rhyme with the words the teacher has given them.

Recommended reading:

(rhyming poems)

Dressing up by John Coldwell

A hat by Colin West

Why I'm always going to wear my baseball cap by David Harmer

Nightclothes by Steve Turner

Nine reasons for hating children by Fred Sedgwick

Rhyming words are fun to read!

1 Circle the parts of the words that rhyme in each line.

(a) **sock**   **dock**   **block**   **flock**

(b) **flap**   **trap**   **nap**   **chap**

(c) **moon**   **soon**   **noon**   **swoon**

(d) **table**   **fable**   **cable**   **gable**

School makes me drool!

2 Read this poem.

Jack vs Jill

When Jack and Jill walked up the hill,
    were they having a row?
Did Jill say, 'Jack you hold the pail!'
    And Jack say, 'No, not now!'

Did Jack and Jill then have some words?
    Did Jill get really mad?
Did she think, 'I will get him back!
    He's such a horrid lad!'

When they had made their bucket full,
    and were on their way back,
Did Jill stick out her foot and say,
    'Oh do be careful Jack!'

Did Jack go tumbling down the slope,
    and all because of Jill?
Did he hang on her ponytail,
    and pull her down the hill?

A pail of water they had none,
    and Jill began to cry.
'My crown got broke', said Prince Jack,
    'and my bucket's dry!'

'So, stop your sniffling, let's go up,
    Cook is making a tart.'
So Jack and Jill went up the hill,
    but at least five metres apart.

3 Underline the words that rhyme in the same colour.
Circle the parts that rhyme.

Nothing rhymes with silver or orange!

4 Write three rhyming words for each sound.

(a) – ack	(b) – ate	(c) – ight

Starting with ...

Objective

Learn about the sounds associated with the beginning of a word or syllable

Activities covered

- Matching pictures and sounds
- Matching sounds in a poem
- Writing sounds

Background information

The pupils are learning about sounds and therefore there should be much discussion and oral work in this lesson. The teacher should decide whether to focus on initial sounds or to include initial blends as well.

Before the lesson

Prepare lists of other sounds.

The pupils can come up with words starting with each sound.

The lesson

1. Give the class a specific sound and they can say words that start with that sound, or give words and have the pupils identify the beginning sounds. All examples should be written on the board and left for the duration of the lesson.
2. The pupils match the four sounds to the pictures.
3. The pupils match the beginning sounds of words in the poem to pictures that have the same beginning sounds. Some pupils may require assistance with this. Others may need to be told which words in the poem to match.
4. The pupils write the sounds next to the pictures.
5. The pupils write other beginning sounds.

Answers

1. tr – tree   d – duck
   gl – gloves   ch – chair
2. flower – farm/for   hand – hate/has
   ostrich – on   spoon – spaghetti
   umbrella – uncle   rake – really
   plug – place/plate   wizard – worm/was
3. flower – fl/f   hand – h
   ostrich – o   spoon – sp/s
   umbrella – u   rake – r
   plug – pl/p   wizard – w
4. Teacher check

Additional activities

Pupils can:

1. Write short sentences using mainly words that start with the same sounds.
2. Write a paragraph using words that mainly start with the same sounds.
3. Play a sound game, where small groups are given a sound and the members think of as many words as possible starting with that sound.

Homework suggestion

Find as many words at home starting with given sounds as possible.

1 Match the pictures to the beginning sounds.

What sound does your name start with?

| tr | d | gl | ch |

2 (a) Look at each picture and say the word.

(b) Draw a line from each picture to a word in the poem that has the same starting sound.

My uncle has a worm farm,

A place I really hate.

I was invited over for dinner,

Is that spaghetti on my plate?

3 Write the sounds next to the pictures.

4 Write four other sounds words could start with.

_____ _____ _____ _____

Objective

Learn to connect the beginning of words and syllables with their rhyming parts as an auditory and visual exercise

Activities covered

- Matching sounds to make words
- Breaking words
- Writing words
- Rewriting sentences
- Swapping letters around to make words

Background information

In this lesson, pupils should be made aware of the sounds making a word, as they hear it and as they see it. There should be discussion so the pupils can hear the sounds they are reading.

Before the lesson

Prepare examples of similar exercises to introduce the lesson.

The lesson

1. Model a few examples of connecting parts of words orally with the pupils; e.g. what are these sounds? (sm + ack) What if I put them together? (smack)
2. The pupils match sounds to make words to complete Questions 1 and 2.
3. The pupils break the bold words and write them in the box.
4. The pupils place two sounds together to make words.
5. The pupils swap letters around in words so the sentences make sense.
6. The pupils write a nonsense sentence by swapping the letters in words.

Answers

1.–2. Answers should include: chat, net, not, nit, pet, pot, pat, pit, rot, rat, set, sat, sit, that

3. cat = c + at
   fat = f + at
   lot = l + ot
   hot = h + ot
   rat = r + at

4. (a) pit   (b) flat   (c) got
   (d) shut   (e) cot   (f) wet
   (g) quit   (h) jet   (i) trot

5. (a) I got a hat
   (b) Never hit your pet.
   (c) Sit in the hot sun.

6. Example: My bet pat rit me.

Additional activity

Pupils can:

Write nonsense words and sentences by swapping letters in an existing poem or nursery rhyme.

1 Match these sounds to make words:

Say these sounds:
et, it, at, ot, ut

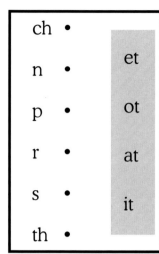

ch •

n •

    et

p •

    ot

r •

    at

s •

    it

th •

2 Write the words you made.

Say them!

3 Break up the words in bold print;
e.g. Jack = J + ack. Write them in the box.

J + ack

Jack is the name of my cat,
He is fluffy, soft and fat,
He sleeps a lot,
When it is hot,
Too lazy to catch a rat.

4 Write these words.   (a) p + it = _____

Say the words!

(b) fl + at = _____   (c) g + ot = _____

(d) sh + ut = _____   (e) c + ot = _____

(f) w + et = _____   (g) qu + it = _____

(h) j + et = _____   (i) tr + ot = _____

5 These words have mixed-up letters! Rewrite the sentences.

(a) I hot a gat. _____

(b) Never pit your het. _____

(c) Sot in the hit sun. _____

6 Swap the beginning letters of the words in bold to create a nonsense sentence.

My **pet rat bit** me. _____

Objective

Learn about common word endings, word families and roots of words

Activities covered

- Finding *'ing'* words in a poem
- Writing root words
- Writing words with *'ing'*
- Adding *'ing'* to words
- Matching pictures and words

Background information

Explain to the pupils what a root word is. (It is the simplest form of the word, and an example can be given, such as 'watch' – from this root word we can get 'watching', 'watches', 'watched' and 'watchful'). Many examples can be done orally as a class. Use each word being discussed in context so the pupils hear when the particular form is used.

Before the lesson

Prepare a list of root words from which the pupils must make other words.

The lesson

1. Discuss examples of root words with the class and ask the pupils to say words that are derived from each.
2. Read the poem ***Boarding*** with the class. Difficult words, such as 'boarding', can be discussed.
3. The pupils underline all the *'ing'* words.
4. The pupils write the root words for a given list of words.
5. The pupils write two more words with *'ing'*.
6. The pupils add *'ing'* to the given words.
7. The pupils write an *'ing'* word to match each picture.

Answers

1. Boarding, hanging, watching, seeing, feeling, boarding, missing, laughing, talking, sharing, looking, thinking
2.

(a) hang	(b) watch	(c) see
(d) feel	(e) board	(f) miss
(g) laugh	(h) talk	(i) share
(j) look	(k) think	

3. Teacher check
4.

(a) bringing	(b) drying	(c) sleeping
(d) eating	(e) playing	(f) staying

5.

(a) kicking	(b) dancing	(c) painting	(d) building

Additional activities

Pupils can:

1. Complete similar activities using other common word endings, word families and roots of words.
2. Play games in class with the pupils divided into groups. Each group is given a root word and must add prefixes/suffixes etc.
3. Read other material and identify all the *'ing'* or *'ful'* words (wonderful, beautiful) etc.
4. Write a list of activities done in a day, using *'ing'* words.

1 Find all the **'ing'** words in this poem. Underline them.

Boarding

*The moon is hanging
in the jet-black sky,
Is she watching me now,
seeing me cry?*

*I'm feeling so lonely
in this boarding school,
The teachers are aliens,
the kids are just cruel.*

*I'm missing my home,
the laughing and fun,
The talking and sharing,
where here there is none.*

*My family are looking
at the same bright moon,
Are they thinking of me?
Will they fetch me soon?*

2 Write the root words.

hanging	watching	seeing
_____	_____	_____
feeling	boarding	missing
_____	_____	_____
laughing	talking	sharing
_____	_____	_____
looking	thinking	
_____	_____	

3 Write two more words ending with **'ing'**.

_____ _____

4 Add **'ing'** to these words.

(a) bring _____

(b) dry _____

(c) sleep _____

(d) eat _____

(e) play _____

(f) stay _____

5 Write the correct **'ing'** word for each picture.

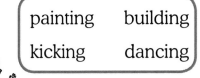

painting   building

kicking   dancing

(a) _____

(b) _____

(c) _____

(d) _____

Big words

Objective

Identify what people in different occupations do

Activities covered

- Listening to a poem
- Discussing difficult words, identifying clues
- Drawing pictures to show meanings of words
- Writing plurals

Background information

Pupils need to be equipped with strategies to work out unfamiliar words, by using their knowledge of sounds to sound out words and by looking at the text around the words to see if there are any clues. The poem in this lesson is quite difficult, with some long words, but the clues will make it easier to work out what the words mean. Discuss the poem with the class at length, and the various occupations mentioned in it. The pupils should say the unfamiliar words aloud, using their knowledge of sound-letter relationships.

Pupils should not be expected to learn these difficult words.

Before the lesson

Prepare some pictures of people in the occupations mentioned in the poem.

The lesson

1. Read the poem **Looks** to the class.
2. Discuss the unfamiliar words, asking what each person might do in his/her occupation and what the clues are that give this information. Words that could be discussed include 'carpenter', 'mechanic', 'hood', 'veterinarian', 'angler', 'decorator', 'plumber', 'artisan', 'archaeologist', 'ancient', 'meteorologist', 'cardiologist', 'astrologer', 'publican', 'stockbroker', 'profit', 'loss'.
3. The pupils draw pictures to show the given occupations.
4. The pupils write plurals for the given words.

Answers

1.–2. Teacher check

3. (a) stars   (b) pets   (c) brushes   (d) boxes
    (e) rocks   (f) hearts   (g) buses   (h) teachers
    (i) wood   (j) tools

Additional activities

Pupils can:

1. Attempt to read unfamiliar words by looking at the surrounding text; e.g. in a poem. Unfamiliar words in other subjects can be worked out using the same strategies.
2. Look up their own more difficult words, and give a clue to the class/group as to what each word means. The class can then try to guess.

Homework suggestion

Find an unfamiliar word in a newspaper or magazine and try to identify the word using the taught strategies. Report back to the class.

1 Listen to this poem.

Looks

A carpenter looks for pieces of wood,   An archaeologist looks out for ancient rocks,

An American mechanic looks under the hood,   A meteorologist looks up weather charts,

A veterinarian looks after a sickly pet,   A cardiologist looks upon human hearts,

An angler looks at his rods and net,   An astrologer looks up at a star,

A decorator looks for her paint and brush,   A publican looks around his bar,

A plumber looks at why the toilet won't flush, A stockbroker looks at profit and loss,

An artisan looks into his big toolbox,   And my schoolteacher? She just looks cross!

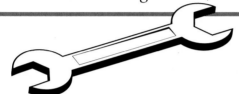

> Where do geologists go
> for entertainment?
> Rock concerts!

2 Draw pictures to show what these people do.

(a)	(b)	(c)
mechanic	teacher (They don't just shout!)	meteorologist

3 Write plurals (more than one).

star _____   pet _____

brush _____   box _____

rock _____   heart _____

bus _____   teacher _____

wood _____   tool _____

Objective

Self-correct reading errors when what he/she reads does not make sense

Activities covered

- Reading poem to a partner
- Taking note of mistakes
- Improving on reading
- Reading poem together
- Making list
- Reading list

Background information

Pupils should often get the opportunity to read aloud, in a class, group or pair situation. They should always be encouraged to correct themselves; the teacher or classmates should only help if the reader is struggling. Poetry with rhythm is good for this type of lesson because a certain amount of fluency is required so as not to lose that rhythm. Most importantly, struggling readers should never be made to feel embarrassed, but rather encouraged in a friendly and helpful environment.

Recommended reading:

(For fluency)

Busy day by Michael Rosen

Please Mrs Butler by Allan Ahlberg

Before the lesson

The class will be divided into pairs.

The teacher can have other short examples of rhythmic poetry.

The lesson

1. The teacher can read the poem ***Fright night*** with the class and discuss any unfamiliar words.
2. The pupils take it in turns to read the poem ***Fright night*** to their partner.
3. Partners make notes on the poem where the other makes mistakes (if there are any!).
4. The pupils show each other where they made mistakes.
5. The pupils correct their mistakes.
6. Pairs read the poem together.
7. The pupils write a list of scary words.
8. Partners read the list to each other.
9. If the teacher has other examples of poetry to read, this can be done.

Answers

1.–8. Teacher check

Additional activities

Pupils can:

1. Read Dr Seuss books, which are excellent for gaining fluency in reading.
2. Be involved in a 'buddy reading scheme' whereby weaker readers are helped by stronger readers for a specified time each week.

Homework suggestion

Read the same poem as fluently as possible to a family member.

Sometimes we make mistakes when we read, and that's OK! We should correct our mistakes and keep going.

Do not read fast!

Fright night

I was invited to a party,
Just the other night,
I thought that it would be some fun,
But it was a fright night!

The door was opened by a witch,
Who was holding a big broom,
I thought she looked a little odd,
But then I looked around the room.

I saw Dracula and zombies,
A pale and spooky ghost,
But it was the wrapped-up mummies,
That frightened me the most.

There were werewolves and a wizard,
Monsters, slimy and green.
Dancing, bony skeletons,
And a goblin that looked mean.

I felt a little out of place,
When they all went to howl at the moon,
But before you say 'It's Halloween!'
This was the 6th of June!

1 Read this poem to your partner. Correct your own mistakes as you go.

2 Your partner must mark on the poem where you went wrong and corrected yourself.

3 Show each other your mistakes and try to correct them.

4 Read the poem together, trying not to make any mistakes.

5 How many mistakes did you make?

6 Write a list of scary words.

_____

_____

_____

7 Give the list to your partner to read through carefully, without making mistakes!

8 How did you do?

What is a ghost's favourite game?
Hide and shriek!

Teacher's pet

Objective

Develop reading skills through engaging with reading material appropriate to his/her stage of development

Activities covered

- Reading a poem
- Answering questions
- Rating a poem for ease of reading

Background information

Reading should be an enjoyable experience and not a chore! Teachers should, where possible, keep reading material fun or interesting and always age-appropriate. In this lesson, read the poem through with the class but do not initiate discussion, giving the pupils the opportunity to read the poem and answer the questions on their own.

Before the lesson

Prepare other suitable poems to read with the class.

The lesson

1. Read a selection of other poems with the pupils.
2. Read the poem **Teacher's pet** while the pupils follow. Clarify difficult words such as 'annoying', 'politely', 'vanished', but do not initiate any discussion. Read through the questions but do not discuss them.
3. The pupils read the poem on their own and answer Questions 2–4.
4. Discuss the poem and questions as a class; e.g. 'What does "teacher's pet" usually mean?'
5. The pupils rate the poem on the scale depending on how easy or difficult it is to read.

Answers

1. Teacher check
2. (a) hamster　　(b) cake　　　(c) quiet
   (d) never　　　(e) neat
3.–5. Teacher check

Additional activities

Pupils can:

1. Read some of the following—poetry, comics, jokes, magazines, websites.
2. Complete a variety of wordsearches and crossword puzzles.
3. Make a display in the classroom of all the things the class has enjoyed reading.
4. Design a 'lost' poster, perhaps using ideas from the poem; e.g. neat hamster, likes history.

Homework suggestion

Read a selected poem for homework.

Websites:

(reading material)
<www.sundhagen.com/babbooks>
<www.magickeys.com/books>

1 Read the poem below on your own.

Teacher's pet

The teacher's pet is annoying,
The whole class will agree.
For lunch she always gives him cake,
And even shares her tea!

He hardly ever makes a sound,
But listens to every word,
You would think that the teacher,
Was the greatest thing he'd heard.

He never leaves things in a mess,

He does not fight or swear.
He always eats politely,
He never scrapes his chair.

Our teacher says if we behaved like him,
Then she would never shout,
But oops! I think he's vanished!
Who let the hamster out???

2 Circle the correct word.

(a) The teacher's pet is a (**boy**, **hamster**, **sheep**).

(b) The teacher always gives him (**bread**, **popcorn**, **cake**).

(c) The teacher's pet is (**noisy**, **quiet**, **cheeky**).

(d) He is (**never**, **always**, **often**) in trouble.

(e) The teacher's pet is (**neat**, **messy**, **grumpy**).

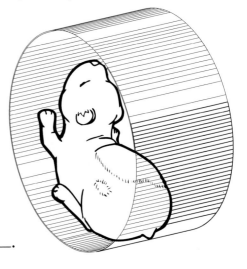

3 Complete this sentence:

The teacher's pet does not

_____ or _____ .

4 Where do you think the teacher's pet might have gone?

_____

5 How easy was the poem to read? Mark it on the scale.

EASY   DIFFICULT

Teachers notes

Objective

Listen to and read a poem, then answer questions about it

Activities covered

- Listening to the teacher reading a poem quickly
- Scanning a poem for information
- Answering questions

Background information

This lesson is intended to make the pupils scan something they are reading. The teacher should explain that when we scan a text we are reading quickly but at the same time trying to remember important points.

A time limit should be set by the teacher when the pupils are scanning a text.

Before the lesson

Prepare an example of scanning a text to do together as a class.

The lesson

1. Read the poem **Can't wait** quickly with the pupils following.
2. Discuss the more difficult words in the poem, such as 'shots' (slang for injections), 'on the beat', 'criminals', 'fame'.
3. The pupils read the poem with a time limit.
4. The pupils cover the poem and answer Question 2. These questions should be answered individually. Read the questions to the pupils if necessary.
5. The class can read the poem together again and check how many answers they got correct.
6. The lesson can be summed up with a class discussion.

Answers

1. Teacher check
2. (a) give injection/shot
   (b) keep street safe/round up criminals
   (c) doughnuts
   (d) write a book
   (e) homework
   (f) 100
   (g) friends/fame/riches
3. Teacher check

Additional activities

Pupils can:

1. 'Scan' the classroom for a given amount of time. They then close their eyes and are asked questions about the classroom.
2. 'Scan' advertisements, nonfiction books, a picture with details etc. and answer questions about the details.
3. Browse through books during silent reading time.

1 Listen to this poem, then read it yourself. Concentrate!

Can't wait

When I am all grown up,
I want to be a vet,
I will help all little creatures,
And give shots to your pet.

No, I think I would rather be,
A police officer on the beat,
I will round up all the criminals,
Bring safety to your street.

Actually, on second thoughts,
I think I will be a cook,
I'll make some doughnuts on TV,
And even write a book.

Or maybe I will be a teacher,
I will give homework every night,
I would make kids do sums 100 times,
Until they got them right.

A pop star sounds even better,
I will have riches and also fame,
I will have many important friends,
All would know my name.

I just can't wait to grow up,
To be what I can be,
The world will be a better place,
And all because of me.

Do not peek!

2 Cover the poem and answer these questions.

(a) What will the vet do for your pet?

_____

(b) What will the police officer do?

_____

(c) What will the cook make? _____

(d) What else will the cook do? _____

(e) What will the teacher give every day? _____

(f) How many times will children have to do their sums? _____

(g) Name two things the pop star will have.

┌──────────────────────────┐   ┌──────────────────────────┐
│   │   │   │
└──────────────────────────┘   └──────────────────────────┘

3 Read the poem again and check how many you got right.   ┌──────────┐
                                                              │   │
                                                              └──────────┘

Objective

Experience a classroom environment that encourages writing

Activities covered

- Reading a poem and guessing its subject
- Choosing a topic
- Writing a six-line poem
- Reading a poem to the class

Background information

Pupils should receive encouragement when writing and this can be achieved through positive feedback from the teacher and the pupil seeing his/her writing has some value. Displays of writing should be in the classroom as well as in areas where the whole school can see them. Pupils can also keep portfolios of their written work. Teachers can hand out awards that don't focus only on the academic side, such as 'Most Original Work' or 'Best Improvement'.

Before the lesson

An example of another six-line poem could be written to further explain the concept to the pupils.

The lesson

1. Explain to the class how the six-line poem works and read the example given.
2. The pupils choose their topic and write a six-line poem.
3. The pupils read their poem to the class. The class tries to guess which person is being described.
4. The pupils rewrite their poem neatly or type it and draw a picture to go with it.

Answers

1.–3. Teacher check

Additional activities

Pupils can:

1. Pick the name of a class member out of a 'hat'. Write a card or letter to that person.
2. Choose a member of their family and write a six-line poem about him/her, focusing on the nice points. Read it to him/her for homework.

1 Read the poem which uses six lines to describe a person. Can you guess who this poem describes?

COLOUR	*He is snow-white*
WEATHER	*He is cold, icy rain*
FURNITURE	*He is a black, leather chair*
PLACE	*He is a hospital ward*
CLOTHING	*He is a white coat*
TYPE OF FOOD	*He is a cool cup of coffee*

2 Write one of your own to describe a person, such as a nurse, teacher or builder etc.

Who do you choose? _____

Don't make it too obvious!

Colour _____

Weather _____

Furniture _____

Place _____

Clothing _____

Type of food _____

3 (a) Read your poem to the class and see if they can guess the person.
Did they guess correctly?

☐ Yes ☐ No

(b) How could you make your poem easier to understand?

_____

_____

Recipe

Objective

Observe the teacher as he/she models writing poems

Activities covered

- Observing the teacher model writing a recipe
- Reading a recipe
- Writing a recipe

Background information

The teacher is often the one modelling stories, poetry etc. In this lesson, the teacher can give an example of a recipe; (e.g. 'recipe to turn pupils into angels'), drawing on the pupils' ideas and, if necessary, improving words and sentences. The recipe, with a list of ingredients and a method, can be written on the board and left as an example.

Before the lesson

Show pupils real recipes and discuss their format.

The lesson

1. The teacher writes a recipe for something (see 'Background information'), getting ideas from the pupils.
2. The pupils read **Recipe for peace**.
3. The pupils write their own recipe. Tell the pupils their recipes need not be written in verse nor rhyme. They can then display their recipes in the classroom.

Answers

1.–2. Teacher check

Additional activity

Pupils can:

Observe modelling of various writing tasks, such as stories, poems, lists, diaries, paragraphs, captions etc.

1 Read the recipe below.
   (Would you be in the pot?)

Recipe for peace

Get a big and bubbling cauldron,
And make it very hot,
Throw in some naughty children,
And some salt into the pot.

Mix gently and ignore the screams,
Add some herbs and spice,
Cover and boil for about half an hour,
And serve on a bed of rice.

The black pot
a witch may
use is called
a cauldron.

2 Write your own recipe!

What is your recipe for? _____

Words you might use:
mix, stir, blend, fry,
boil, simmer, bake,
roast, steam, grill,
whisk, beat, chop, slice

Ingredients:	Method:

Objective

Seek help from the teacher in order to achieve accuracy and an appropriate standard of presentation

Activities covered

- Reading an example of a simple poem
- Writing an **'I used to be'** poem
- Conferring with the teacher

Background information

The main purpose of this lesson is for teachers to check the pupils' work and point out mistakes and/or ways to improve it. The pupils can then rewrite their poems, decorate them and display them. The pupils should feel proud to display their work, knowing it has few or no mistakes, and this should boost their confidence. When teachers are helping pupils to edit their work, they should be sensitive and praise the good points too!

Before the lesson

Make sure there is enough time to check all the pupils' work with them.

The lesson

1. Explain to the pupils that they will be writing a poem.
2. Read **I used to be** while the class follows.
3. Pupils write one way the child has changed.
4. The pupils write a poem using the starting sentences provided.
5. Discuss each pupil's poem with him/her. Point out any mistakes and ways he/she could improve his/her poem.
6. The pupils can rewrite their poem neatly and decorate it.
7. Display all the poems in the classroom.

Answers

1. Teacher check
2. taller/better at sports/eats bread/can spell/switches light off/ cleaner/leaves bugs alone/better behaved
3. Teacher check

Additional activity

Pupils can:

Have their writing activities checked, especially those that will be displayed.

Homework suggestion

Show their poem to family members.

As we grow up, we change.

1 Read how this child has changed.

> I used to be short and little,
> but now I am so tall,
> I used to be bad at sports,
> but now I'm good with the ball.
> I used to be weak at my spelling,
> but now I can do most,
> I used to be sick at the sight of bread,
> but now I live on toast!
>
> I used to be afraid of the dark,
> but now I switch off the light,
> I used to be so sloppy and messy,
> but now my shirts stay white.
> I used to keep bugs in clear glass jars,
> but now I leave them free,
> I used to be a naughty kid,
> but now I'm a different me!

2 Write one way the child has changed.

_____

3 Write a poem like the one above about yourself:

I used to be _____

but now _____

I used to be _____

but now _____

I used to be _____

but now _____

I used to be _____

but now _____

I used to be _____

but now _____

Objective

Experience how a story structure is organised by reading and listening to fiction

Activities covered

- Reading with the teacher
- Drawing pictures
- Showing the beginning, middle and end of a story

Background information

In this lesson, a poem is used instead of a story. The pupils need to be made aware that a story often has a beginning, a middle and an end. Many well-known fairytales can be used to illustrate this; e.g. 'How does the story of *Cinderella* start?' 'How does *The three little pigs* end?' The pupils can then use a beginning, middle and an end when writing their own stories.

Before the lesson

Provide examples of different well-known stories. The class can discuss the beginning, middle and end of each.

The lesson

1. Discuss various stories with the pupils.
2. Read ***Honestly*** to the pupils. The poem can then be read aloud as a class. Harder words can be discussed, such as 'splendid', 'host' and 'UFO'.
3. Discuss the storyline with the pupils, asking 'what happens in the beginning/middle/end?'
4. The pupils draw the story and show the beginning, middle and end by writing 'B', 'M' or 'E' on the appropriate pictures.

Answers

1.–3. Teacher check

Additional activities

Pupils can:

1. Discuss and write about story lines in other poems, short stories, class readers, or TV programmes.
2. Write the beginning or end of a selected fairytale.

Usually, a story has a beginning, a middle and an end.

1 Read this with your teacher.

2 Tell this story in pictures.

Honestly!

BEGINNING

Yesterday I wasn't at school, Miss,
And I am going to tell you why,
And this is all the truth, Miss,
For you know I wouldn't lie.

MIDDLE

I had some important guests,
Who dropped by to visit me,
Yes, a bunch of ugly aliens,
Dropped in for a cup of tea.

Then they wanted breakfast,
I gave them beans on toast,
I made them feel quite welcome,
I was a splendid host.

They wanted to have a bath then,
And to use the telephone,
I was dying to get to school, Miss,
But I could not leave them alone.

END

The whole day I looked after them,
They just did not want to go,
I'm afraid they stole my homework, Miss,
It's now on their UFO!

UFO stands for Unidentified Flying Object.

3 Show the beginning (B), the middle (M) and the end (E) of the story by writing the correct letters on your pictures.

A card says it all

Objective

Write regularly for different audiences

Activities covered

- Writing and designing a card
- Making a card using cardboard

Background information

Pupils should practise writing for different audiences, being aware that the tone may differ, depending on who they are writing for. The teacher can use examples of different cards and ask pupils who they think the cards might be intended for. The teacher can ask the pupils questions to initiate thinking; e.g. 'How would a card to a friend be different from a card to the prime minister?' Sometimes the tone will be relaxed and at other times the tone might be formal. Pupils should see examples of this. For this lesson, pupils are making cards for a particular person; they need not be for a special occasion. It is important that pupils are able to give/send their cards to the person they are intended for.

Recommended reading:

Pupils read a variety of greeting cards.

Websites:

(making cards)

<www.ivyjoy.com/printcards>

<www.allcrafts.net/cards.htm>

Before the lesson

The teacher has examples of different cards. Even Christmas cards can be used as they come in a variety of different 'tones', from cheerful and relaxed to elegant and formal.

The lesson

1. The class discusses the cards which the teacher has brought in, including the different occasions and for whom they might be suitable.
2. Discuss with the pupils different 'tones' that may be used for different audiences.
3. Pupils do a rough sketch of their card. They can draw pictures, add a verse and create a border
4. Once pupils have a clear idea of what they want their card to look like, they can create it on quality paper or card. The pupils should think about the person they are making the card for. They should create the card for that specific person to enjoy.
5. Pupils must give/send their card to the person for whom it was made.

Answers

1.–5. Teacher check

Additional activity

Pupils can:

Perform a variety of writing tasks, aimed at different audiences; e.g. a speech to the school, a talk (for children their own age and for younger children), a note to a babysitter, a letter to a famous person.

Homework suggestion

Bring a greeting card to school. These can be displayed in the classroom. (Teachers should make sure there are no personal messages inside these!)

You are going to make a card to give to someone special.

1 Who will you make your card for? _____

2 Write a two-line poem for the inside of your card; for example,

> *This is just a note to say*
>
> *Hope you have a wonderful day!*

Use the word bank to help you.

_____

_____

Word bank

hope	wishes
luck	well
sorry	best
congratulations	
moving	regards
birthday	wedding
friend	thank you
sympathy	

3 In the space below, plan a design for the front of your card.

HAPPY BIRTHDAY

4 Try to improve your design. When you are happy with it, make your card.

5 Colour a face to show how you feel about your finished card.

A thing

Objective
Write a poem to describe something

Activities covered
- Reading a description poem
- Drawing an answer
- Describing a chosen 'thing' as a poem
- Reading a description poem to class

Background information
Pupils should frequently be given the opportunity to choose their own topics to write about, whether for a story, poem, letter etc. They will often choose topics they know a lot about and/or which interest them; this gives them more confidence with the writing task.

Before the lesson
A teacher-devised example of another description poem should be prepared.

The lesson
1. Read the teacher-prepared example of a description poem with the class. The class can write a similar poem together.
2. The pupils can then read the **Moon** poem and answer Question 2. The pupils choose a topic to write about. They should not discuss their topic with anyone as the class will have to guess what it is later.
3. The pupils write their own poem describing their object in as many ways as they can. No rhyming is necessary. They should write sentences as in the example.
4. The pupils read their poem, first to themselves and then to the class, while the class tries to guess what the 'thing' is. The pupils complete Question 5.

Answers
1. Teacher check
2. moon
3.–5. Teacher check

Additional activity
Pupils can:

Choose their own topics when writing letters, stories, poems, rhymes, sentences, advertisements, instructions, lists etc.

Homework suggestion
Read finished poems to a family member.

1 Read the poem below.

> A cow jumped over it.
>
> It shines brightly.
>
> It can be a full circle.
>
> Men have walked on it.
>
> It rhymes with 'spoon'.
>
> I can see it from my bedroom window.
>
> It looks white or yellow.
>
> Sometimes it is a banana shape.

School is not my thing.

2 Can you guess what this 'thing' is? Draw your answer.

3 Select an animal, a piece of clothing or anything else you choose to describe.

What thing did you choose? _____

4 In the space below, write a poem that describes the thing you chose in as many ways as you can.

These should all be sentences!

_____

_____

_____

_____

_____

_____

5 Read your poem, first to yourself, then to the class.

Did they guess what your 'thing' was? ☐ Yes ☐ No

Letter to a friend

Objective

Explore different genres

Activities covered

- Reading a letter
- Writing a note
- Writing a letter

Background information

Pupils need a variety of writing tasks so that lessons are kept interesting and they are able to work on different skills. The teacher can show pupils the basic format of a letter:

Dear _____,

_____

_____

from _____

Pupils need to be given opportunities to write different types of material for different audiences. In this lesson, pupils must write full sentences.

Before the lesson

The teacher collects examples of letters to show to the pupils.

The lesson

1. The teacher can discuss the format of a letter and several examples can be examined.
2. The teacher and class read the letter and discuss it.
3. The pupils write a note.
4. The pupils write a letter.

Answers

1.–3. Teacher check

Additional activity

Pupils can:

Write the following: an invitation, a menu, a new class timetable, an advertisement, a food label, an envelope, a TV timetable, a recipe, a list, a film review, a game or toy review, instructions for the pet-sitter, an itinerary etc.

Recommended reading:

Pupils read poetry in different forms; e.g.

Knickers by Gina Douthwaite

Dad the amateur hypnotist by Mike Johnson

Basil by Gareth Owen

Do you know my teacher? by John Rice

1 Read the letter Andy has written to his friend.

> *Dear Frank,*
>
> *How are you this wonderful day?*
> *I'm fine myself, I have to say.*
>
> *I wonder whether you would mind –*
> *if you could be so very kind –*
>
> *If my mates and I come visit you,*
> *just for the weekend, that will do.*
>
> *Tell your mother to get ready to bake,*
> *My favourite thing is chocolate cake.*
>
> *We will have a party, it will be great fun.*
> *We will be there on Friday, at about one.*
>
> *So, see you soon, I know you are glad,*
> *don't forget the sweets – good lad!*
>
> *From Andy*

2 Write a short note from Frank to Andy.

Dear Andy,

_____

_____

_____

_____

_____

_____

From Frank

3 On a separate sheet of paper, write a letter to your friend.

Change that rhyme!

Objective

Work with other pupils when writing

Activities covered

- Reading a rhyme
- Reading changed rhymes
- Working as a group to change a rhyme
- Writing out a rhyme

Background information

Working together on writing activities gives pupils the opportunity to discuss their work, help each other, be tolerant of others and contribute to a group. Working in a group also means that pupils do not have sole responsibility for a piece of work. Group structure is important for this activity. Therefore, teachers will have to select groups carefully. It may sometimes be necessary to appoint a group leader. Check that all members of the group are participating in the task.

Before the lesson

Divide the class into small groups.

Another example of a rhyme that can be changed may be provided to show the pupils.

The lesson

1. The class reads **Mary had a little lamb** and then the two changed rhymes.
2. At this stage the pupils could be given another rhyme that can be changed as a whole class. Point out that rhyming patterns should remain the same if possible.
3. In small groups, the pupils change a rhyme by changing some of the words. Pupils can choose a rhyme or the teacher can name one.
4. After discussion, the pupils write the new rhyme as a draft and then try to improve on it.
5. The pupils rewrite their poem neatly and decorate it.
6. All poems can be displayed in the classroom and/or read out to the class.

Answers

1.–3. Teacher check

Additional activities

Pupils can:

1. Complete group projects for another subject, such as history.
2. Write stories in groups, with each member contributing a few lines.
3. In groups, write cartoon strips on a given topic.
4. In groups, write very short plays about an everyday experience, (e.g. going to school). Each member in the group can be responsible for one character's lines.

Website:

<www.rhymes.org.uk >

Change that rhyme!

1 Read this well-known nursery rhyme.

'Mary had a little lamb' is an American song from 1830.

> Mary had a little lamb,
> Its fleece was white as snow.
> Everywhere that Mary went,
> The lamb was sure to go!

Mary, where are you?

If some of the words were changed, it could read:

> Mary had a little mouse,
> Whom she spoiled with fancy teas.
> Her family are quite angry,
> As now there's never any cheese!

OR

> Mary had a big, wild lion,
> He loved to lie in the sun.
> One day the teacher stepped on him,
> Now a teacher they have none!

2 In a small group, change a nursery rhyme. Try to use the same rhyming pattern. Write it below.

_____

_____

_____

_____

_____

_____

_____

3 Try to improve on your poem. Copy out your poem neatly and decorate it.

Objective

Have writing valued

Activities covered

- Discussing poem style and an example
- Writing a five-line poem
- Assessing a poem

Background information

A cinquain is supposed to have a set number of syllables, but to simplify it, in this lesson the pupils have to use a specific number of words. Go through the 'formula' step by step with the pupils and perhaps write a poem as a class together, describing the teacher! All attempts should be praised and all poems displayed. For the poem, pupils must focus on positive characteristics.

Before the lesson

A teacher-devised example could be prepared to show the class.

The lesson

1. Go through the style of poem step by step with the pupils. The class can do one together, describing the teacher. This example can be left on the board.
2. The pupils read the example *Jason*.
3. The pupils write their own five-line poem, then read it to themselves and assess it.

Answers

1.–3. Teacher check

Additional activities

Pupils can:

1. Value their work in the following ways: classroom displays, school bulletin board displays, having outsiders look at their work, taking it home to show family members, a school gallery of writing, weekly achievement awards, use of portfolios, sharing with others in group etc.
2. Write the same five-line poem about a family member, saying nice things only! The poem can then be presented to the family member for homework.

Websites:

(ideas for reinforcement)
<www.childdevelopmentinfo.com/parenting/
communication.shtml>
(ideas for parents but teachers can use
them too!)

1 Write a poem that is about you! Be kind to yourself! Your poem should follow this pattern.

Line 1 – Title (Your name)

Line 2 – 2 words describing yourself

Line 3 – 3 action words
(What do you enjoy doing?)

Line 4 – 4 words about your feelings

Line 5 – Another name you go by

Example:

Jason

short, handsome,

skateboarding, eating, singing

wish I was home

JT

2 Write your poem in the space below.

Line 1:

_____

Line 2:

_____

Line 3:

_____

Line 4:

_____

Line 5:

_____

3 Read your poem to yourself. What do you think of it?

Make it exciting

Objective

Experiment with more elaborate vocabulary and sentence structure in order to extend and explore meaning

Activities covered

- Describing objects
- Adding words to a poem
- Rewriting a poem

Background information

This lesson should be an oral lesson—therefore, the whole class can participate. The pupils need to be reminded to make their own writing more interesting by adding better words and using longer sentences. New words that are encountered should be written in the pupils' personal word book to be referred to when doing their own writing. New words can also be displayed in the classroom on a 'New Word Wall'.

Before the lesson

Prepare some simple sentences to which the pupils can add details to make them more interesting. These examples can be completed as a class at the beginning of the lesson.

The lesson

1. The teacher can give the pupils a few very simple sentences and, as a class, the pupils can elaborate on them; e.g. 'The boy jumped.' / 'The lady cried.' / 'The dragon bit.'
2. The pupils read the two given sentences and decide which is more interesting. Ask the class what makes it more interesting.
3. The pupils come up with a list of describing words to describe the given things for Question 2.
4. Read the poem on the page as a class.
5. The pupils add details to the poem where indicated by the arrows. This can be done individually and then the poem can be discussed as a class. The pupils can then rewrite their own poems and improve on them if necessary.
6. The pupils answer Question 5.
7. Poems can be rewritten and displayed in the classroom.

Answers

1. Answers should indicate that (b) is more interesting because it gives us more detail or information.
2.–5. Teacher check

> Example for number 3:
> *My black and white, fluffy cat,*
> *Will daily bring a half-dead rat,*
> *She always puts it on my clean, fresh bed,*
> *I wish she'd bring a sweet rose instead!*

Additional activities

Pupils can:

1. Replace the word 'nice' with more interesting words when writing; e.g. nice day – great day, nice game – exciting game, nice sandwich – tasty sandwich, nice night – warm night.
2. Describe an object orally to their group, adding as much detail as possible. The group can then guess the object.
3. Think up as many describing words for a given object as they can. These can then be discussed as a class.

*Our writing can be more interesting
if we add details.*

I'm not just a cat!
I'm fluffy, soft, cute
and clever!

1 Read these sentences and circle the
one you think is more interesting.

  (a) My cat attacks my toes!

  (b) My crazy cat attacks my poor little
       toes when I am watching TV!

2 Describe each of these using three different describing words.

  (a) monster _____

  (b) school _____

  (c) chips _____

  (d) football _____

3 Make the poem below more
interesting by adding words. The
arrows ↓ suggest where you could
place words.

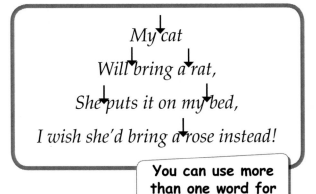

My↓cat
Will↓bring a↓rat,
She↓puts it on my↓bed,
I wish she'd bring a↓rose instead!

**You can use more
than one word for
each arrow!**

4 Rewrite the poem here.
Improve on it if you need to!

5 Which poem sounds better?

  ☐ With details ☐ Without details

Objective

Focus on the subject under discussion and sustain a conversation about it

Activities covered

- Reading a poem
- Discussing a poem
- Answering questions
- Telling the class about his/her own home
- Discussing what a home should have/feel like

Background information

Pupils can be easily side-tracked, often wanting to tell stories about things that happened to them. The topic in this lesson is homes and the pupils must stick to the subject—make sure they are told this. Write keywords on the board as they arise so that at the end of the lesson, the board is full of words to do with the topic of 'homes'. Make sure the pupils are not placed in an awkward position by comparing their homes—just the basics are required.

Recommended reading:

My room by Steve Turner
Coming home by Steve Turner

Before the lesson

A list of different types of homes and/or pictures of them could be prepared.

The lesson

1. The pupils read the poem *Home sweet home* together.
2. The poem is discussed as a class.
3. As a class, the pupils answer Question 2. (Full sentences are not necessary.)
4. The pupils take turns to tell a little bit of information about their own home. (Limit the time each speaks.)
5. The class can talk about different homes.
6. In pairs, the pupils discuss what a home should have and what a home should feel like. They then write some of the ideas they came up with. These could be reported back to the class.

Answers

1. Teacher check
2. (a) old
   (b) warm, cosy, delicious smells, table, chair
   (c) no   (d) yes
3. Teacher check
   Discussion of homes could include: tent, apartment, igloo, house, caravan, bungalow, mobile home, tepee, log cabin, cottage, houseboat, castle, chalet, penthouse, detached, semi-detached, terraced, flat, duplex, unit, farm, homestead
4. Answers may include some of the following:
   What a home should have: beds, place to eat, bath or shower, toilet, chair or place to rest (only necessities should be included here, not what pupils actually have in their own homes)
   What a home should feel like: comfortable, warm, safe, inviting, relaxing, cosy, friendly, welcoming

Additional activities

Pupils can:

1. Repeat the same type of lesson (i.e. discussion and conversation) in other subjects, such as science, history or geography.
2. Make a display in the classroom of different types of houses.

Homework suggestion

Draw and label their home and show their favourite spots.

Home sweet home

Have you heard this saying?
'There's no place like home.'

Home is where
the ♥ is.

1 Read the poem.

Home sweet home

My house is not very big,
and it's also rather old.
It was built in the 1800s,
or so I have been told.

The kitchen is warm and cosy,
with delicious smells in the air,
a large and wooden table,
and a creaky rocking chair.

My bedroom is quite messy,
but I love my comfy bed,
my soft and puffy pillows,
to lay my sleepy head.

This place can be quite noisy,
it is a home, you see.
A place where I can laugh and cry,
a place where I am me.

2 As a class, answer these questions:

(a) Is the house new or old? _____

(b) Name one thing that is special about the kitchen. _____

(c) Is the speaker neat and tidy? ☐ Yes ☐ No

(d) Do you think the speaker likes the house? ☐ Yes ☐ No

3 Take turns to tell the class a little about your home.

4 With a partner, write some ideas about:

What a home should have.	What a home should feel like.

Objective

Engage in personal reading

Activities covered

- Choosing a poem
- Copying a poem or part of it
- Answering questions
- Reading out a poem

Background information

Unfortunately, many pupils do not read unless they have to. Pupils need to be encouraged to read for their own personal enjoyment; therefore, it does not matter if the reading material is a story, comic book, nonfiction book, magazine, website, whatever. It is only once pupils are reading frequently that they will gain confidence in reading.

Before the lesson

The pupils will need a poem they have chosen from a poetry anthology or website.

The lesson

1. Before this lesson, the pupils will have read through several poems and chosen one they like.
2. The pupils copy the poem they have chosen onto the sheet. If it is too long, they need only write one or two verses.
3. The pupils answer Questions 2 to 6.
4. The pupils display their poems in the classroom for others to read. Time must be given for pupils to read these.
5. The pupils can read out their poems to the class.

Answers

1.–6. Teacher check

Additional activity

Pupils can:

Read a variety of texts, depending on interests; e.g. recipes, magazines, local newspapers, TV guides, poetry, short stories, fact books, annuals. Various types of reading material should be available in the school.

Recommended reading:

Poetry anthologies

The secret lives of teachers
(poems chosen by Brian Moses)

The works series (poems chosen by well-known children's authors)

Website:

<www.poetryzone.ndirect.co.uk/index2.htm>

1 Choose a poem you like and copy it below.

> If your poem is too long, just write one or two verses.

2 What is the title of the poem?

_____

_____

3 Who wrote it?

_____

4 What do you like about the poem?

_____

_____

_____

_____

5 Underline your favourite words or lines.

6 Read out your poem to a small group or the class.

Perfect world

Teachers notes

Objective
Read aloud to share a text with an audience

Activities covered
- Reading a poem as a class
- Circling specific things in a poem
- Taking turns to read a verse in a group
- Reading a poem as a group
- Assessing group reading

Background information
Pupils often need the opportunity to read aloud to their peers to gain confidence in reading. It is also by reading aloud that they can hear the mistakes they make and correct them, with or without help. Reading aloud in a group may be less intimidating than reading alone in front of the whole class. Shared reading in the classroom should be an enjoyable pastime.

Before the lesson
The class should be divided into groups.

The lesson
1. Read the poem **Perfect world** together as a class.
2. The teacher can read the poem quite slowly while the pupils circle things they enjoy in the poem. The teacher should use expression and emphasise certain words so pupils will be able to follow the example.
3. The teacher can also discuss harder words, such as 'settee', 'familiar'.
4. The pupils discuss the poem and decide as a group how they could read it with expression. The teacher could make suggestions, explaining that reading with expression means a way of reading something that shows our feelings.
5. Each person in the group reads a verse with expression. If there are verses left over, these can be read together as a group.
6. The pupils write one word to assess their reading.
7. The pupils read the poem together as a group.
8. The pupils assess their group reading by colouring the appropriate face.

Answers
1.–6. Teacher check

Additional activities
Pupils can:
1. Read an interesting article to the class or a group.
2. Share poems with the class or a group.
3. Share a letter/postcard/greeting card they have received.
4. Read dialogues or plays together.
5. Read a favourite poem to a group.

Homework suggestion
Read the same poem with a family member.

Recommended reading:
(poems suitable for group reading)
One thing in common by Paul Cookson
School tie by Roger Stevens
Who said what by Gervase Phinn

Perfect world

Free ice-creams all day!

Don't you wish you could wake up one morning and find the world was perfect?

1 Read this poem together as a class.

> **Perfect world**
>
> When I woke up this morning,
> The sun was shining bright,
> And it was a Saturday,
> Yes, everything felt right!
>
> I went through to the kitchen,
> To get a bit of food,
> There was bacon, eggs and sausages,
> And Mum in a good mood!
>
> My best programme was on TV,
> So I lay on the settee,
> My sister, who usually bullies me,
> Made me a cup of tea!
>
> Mum gave me some money,
> She said I should buy toys,
> She said she'd take me to a shop,
> Which sold stuff just for boys.
>
> Dad offered to clean my room,
> Which didn't look the best,
> When I tried to stop him, he said,
> 'Son, you need your rest'.
>
> My best friend rang me up,
> And invited me to the lake,
> They were planning a big picnic,
> With plenty of chocolate cake.
>
> Everything was turning out well,
> This day would be so cool,
> Then I heard a familiar voice,
> 'Wake up! It's time for school!'

2 Circle all the things in the poem that you would enjoy.

3 Work in a group. Decide how you could read this poem with expression. Write ideas on the poem to remind you.

4 (a) Take turns to read a verse. If there are verses left over, read them together.

(b) Write a word to tell how you read.

_____

5 Read the poem together as a group to your class.

6 Colour a face to show how well your group read.

Objective

Find information and shares it with others

Activities covered

- Reading a poem
- Completing research about lions
- Writing five facts
- Sharing information with a group

Background information

For this lesson, pupils must be given time to research the information. The lesson is about sharing their information with their group. Pupils must be told to listen quietly and patiently while others are speaking. The topic should not be discussed before the groups get together. A class discussion should only occur once all pupils have contributed to the group's discussion.

Before the lesson

The teacher should collate a list of facts about lions to discuss with the class once the lesson is over.

Pupils will need access to information about lions.

Pupils will need to research to complete this lesson. This may be in the form of a homework activity or could be completed in class.

The pupils will be divided into groups.

The lesson

1. The teacher reads the poem *Hands up* with the class. The topic of lions is not discussed at this point, nor the correct answers to the questions in the poem. As the poem introduces the topic, it may be necessary for the teacher to read it twice.
2. Pupils are given time to research the topic. This could occur before this lesson.
3. Pupils discuss in groups the five facts they learnt about lions. Pupils then attempt to answer the questions in the poem correctly.
4. Pupils write one new fact they learnt from their group. (If no new facts, they can write one after the class discussion.)
5. The topic is discussed as a class.

Answers

1. Teacher check
2. Facts about lions:
   - Very sociable creatures, live in groups called prides
   - They are carnivores
   - Have excellent sight, hearing and sense of smell
   - When a lion is about to charge, it lashes its tail up and down, flattens its ears and simultaneously roars
   - Both males and females roar as a means of communication
   - Usually silent when hunting
   - Vocal calls range from a loud roar to a low, soft, moaning cough
   - Very powerful animals
   - Good jumpers and swimmers
   - Powerful claws are fully retractable
   - Females are the principal killers
   - At the top of the food chain, no natural enemies, biggest enemy is people
   - Hunt mainly at night
3. The correct answers to questions in the poem are: baby lion – cub, lions eat meat, a group is called a pride, biggest enemy is man
4. Teacher check

Additional activities

Pupils can:

1. Ask their family how life was different when they were the pupils' age, for homework, and then share this information with the group.
2. Complete a group project with each pupil contributing something.

Recommended reading:

The Lion by Roald Dahl

Website:

<www.nationalgeographic.com/kids/ creature_feature/0109/lions2.html>

If you see a lion in the wild, don't run! It will think you are prey. Back slowly away.

1 Read this poem together as a class.

Hands up

'The king of the jungle is the topic today,
Let's see how much you know.
You may only speak if your hand is up
Or to the head you'll go!'

'What do we call a baby lion?
Yes, Jane, your hand is up.
Answer the question, quickly, girl!'
'I think, Miss, it's called a pup.'

'No, Jane, pups belong to pooches,
Now what do lions eat?
Oh Jane again, well answer, pet!'
'I think, Miss, it's roast meat.'

'Not roasts, my dear! Lions can't cook!
Now what do we call a group?
Jane, are you sure? Well, spit it out!'
'I think, Miss, it's a troop.'

'No, Jane, monkeys live in troops,
Now, who is a lion's enemy?
Oh Jane, I hope you get this right!'
'I think, Miss, it's a flea.'

'Jane! All lesson your hand is up!
And you simply don't have a clue!'
'I don't know any of the answers, Miss,
I just want to go to the loo!'

Darling, is the roast almost done?

Jane doesn't know much about lions!

2 Find five facts about lions and write them below.

3 Group work: Tell the group what you learnt and discuss all the different facts. See if you can answer the questions in the poem correctly!

Listen carefully while others are speaking!

4 Write one other fact you learnt from your group.

Objective

Perform simple information retrieval tasks

Activities covered

- Looking at a table of contents
- Answering questions about a table of contents
- Discussing as a class

Background information

The pupils need to have practise accessing information presented in a variety of ways. Use examples of everyday items they may come into contact with, such as timetables, weather charts or graphs.

Before the lesson

Collect books that have a 'table of contents'.

The lesson

1. Show the pupils a table of contents in a book and explain its use. An index can also be discussed here. Other words such as 'author' and 'introduction' can be talked about.
2. Read the table of contents on the copymaster.
3. Read the questions, which the pupils then answer without help.
4. Go through the questions with the class. The pupils calculate the number they got right.
5. The pupils look at books with a table of contents and test them by going to various pages.

Answers

1. Teacher check
2. (a) poems about animals   (b) page 3   (c) Chapter 3
   (d) Chapter 6   (e) Peter Poet   (f) Index
   (g) Chapter 7
3. Teacher check

Additional activity

Pupils can:

Read and compare the following information texts: timetables, menus, tables of information, simple graphs, TV guides, weather charts, pictures with labels, adverts, price lists, food labels etc.

Homework suggestion

Try to find a book with a table of contents at home and bring it to school. All the books can be displayed in the classroom.

Recommended reading:

Use poems for comprehension exercises.

Often at the beginning of a book you will find a table of contents. This tells you what is in the book.

1 Read the table of contents.

THE POETRY POT
By Peter Poet

CONTENTS

2 Answer these questions.

(a) What does Chapter 4 contain?

_____

_____

(b) On which page does Chapter 2 start?

_____

(c) In which chapter will you find the poem *The teacher's mad!?*

_____

(d) Where will you find the photos?

_____

(e) Who is the author?

_____

(f) Where will all the poems be listed?

_____

(g) Where will you find a nursery rhyme?

_____

3 Discuss your answers with the class. How many did you get right? ☐

Objective

Read and write acrostic poems

Activities covered

- Discussing with class and partner
- Writing words to do with a topic
- Reading an acrostic poem
- Writing an acrostic poem

Background information

Many lessons begin with oral language as the teacher often introduces a topic through discussion. Oral language is particularly useful before a writing task to get pupils thinking about a topic as well as discussing it and hearing what others have to say. Different perspectives will give the pupils a better idea of the topic. Discussion should be stimulating and relevant and give pupils more confidence with their writing task. This activity focuses on writing an acrostic poem.

Recommended reading:

(about school)

Choosing schools by Angi Holden

Billy McBone by Allan Ahlberg

Starting school by Steve Turner

The painting lesson by Trevor Harvey

Website:

<http://adifferentplace.org/acrostics.htm>

Before the lesson

A list of words to do with school could be prepared to add to the pupils' lists.

The lesson

1. The class will discuss the topic of school and all aspects of it. Guide the discussion but allow the pupils to have their say. It doesn't all have to be positive but shouldn't be all negative either. The pupils will have to show patience and consideration while others are talking.

2. As the discussion takes place, the pupils can write keywords in the box in Question 2.

3. The pupils read the acrostic poem in Question 3 and then attempt to write their own poem using words from Question 2. The term 'acrostic' may need to be explained. The pupils must also be told that their poems do not need to rhyme.

4. The pupil's poems can be written neatly and displayed in the classroom or school and/or shared orally with the class.

Answers

1.–4. Teacher check

Additional activities

Pupils can:

1. Hold discussions before writing a letter, story, poem, recipe etc.
2. Write an advertisement for their school.
3. Write a poem about their school.
4. Write to a pen pal, describing their school.
5. Draw a picture or plan of their school, labelling favourite places.

1 Hold a class discussion about your favourite place—school! You can talk about things you like and dislike.

2 Write words from the discussion in the box below. These words should all be to do with school.

3 Read this acrostic poem about school.

> S – *School day starts, I want to go home,*
>
> C – *Cannot write this silly poem!*
>
> H – *History time, I try my best,*
>
> O – *Oh, no! It's time for a maths test.*
>
> O – *Outside the day is calling me,*
>
> L – *Let me out and set me free!*

4 Write your own acrostic poem using some of your words from the box.

> **Your words do not have to rhyme!**

S – _____

C – _____

H – _____

O – _____

O – _____

L – _____

Make it better!

Objective

Realise that first attempts at writing are not necessarily the finished product and learn to undertake second drafts in order to improve writing

Activities covered

- Looking at redrafting
- Making a rough draft of a poem
- Redrafting a poem
- Writing a poem neatly

Background information

The pupils must be encouraged to read through their work to correct mistakes and improve on their writing. Pupils are often in too much of a hurry to complete their work; therefore, time should be given to check it. The pupils should become very familiar with the routine of drafting a writing task, checking it (or having a teacher or peer check it), redrafting and, only once completely satisfied, writing a final copy. The pupils will then become more aware of their own mistakes and will be able to take more pride in the finished article.

Before the lesson

Prepare examples of how to check written work and redraft it.

Pupil will need to work in pairs in Question 3.

The lesson

1. Look at the example of redrafting as a class. Ask questions such as: 'Do you think the changes improved the poem?'
2. Use other examples of how to check a piece of writing and redraft it.
3. Explain to the pupils how to write a four-line poem and which words should rhyme ('aabb' rhyme scheme).
4. The pupils write their four-line poem.
5. The pupils check their work, reading it carefully and making any amendments. A partner can also check their work.
6. The pupils rewrite their poem neatly or type it out—but only once they are completely satisfied.
7. All poems should be displayed.

Answers

1.– 4. Teacher check

Additional activity

Pupils can:

Redraft almost all writing tasks; e.g. letters, stories, sentences, poems.

When we write something, it is not always correct the first time. Quite often, we need to check it and make it better.

1 Look at this poet's work.

> ### Weekend
>
> At last the week is ~~over~~ done,
>
> Now I can ~~sit in the sun~~ have some fun,
>
> No more teachers, ~~no more work, free at last~~ hip hip hooray,
>
> Just two days to rest ~~all day~~ and play.

Done
Fun
Bun
Sun
Day
Say
Pay
Tray
Play

It may be a little messy but it's only a draft!

2 Write your own poem about the weekend. It must have four lines. The first two lines should rhyme and the second two lines should rhyme. Don't forget the title!

Words

_____

_____

_____

_____

3 Improve it if you can. Check:

- spelling
- rhyme
- content

Ask a partner to check your poem too.

4 When you are 100% happy, write it neatly on a separate sheet of paper. Draw a picture to go with it.

Stop it!

Objective

Understand that the conventions of punctuation help to make meaning clearer in writing

Activities covered

- Discussing capital letters and full stops
- Adding punctuation to given sentences
- Reading with/without punctuation
- Reading a poem
- Adding punctuation to a poem

Background information

This lesson focuses on capital letters and full stops. At this age, pupils should have much practice with the basics of punctuation and should see the use of capital letters and full stops in context. The teacher can use the class reader or a textbook to show how they are used. Some pupils may struggle to remember how to write all the capital letters.

The following should be displayed in the classroom:

- A capital letter is used at the beginning of a sentence.
- A full stop is used at the end of a sentence.
- 'I' is always a capital letter.

Before the lesson

Prepare examples of how punctuation is used to be written on the board.

The lesson

1. Discuss with the class the use of full stops and capital letters at the beginning of a sentence and for the word 'I'.
2. Pupils complete several examples of full sentences on the board.
3. Pupils add punctuation to the three sentences in Question 1.
4. Pupils read a short passage without punctuation. They then add punctuation and read the passage again, deciding which was easier to read.
5. As a class, read the poem *Mum says*. The pupils can then add capital letters and full stops to it, reading it to themselves as they do it. The teacher can read the poem first if necessary.

Answers

1. (a) Our teacher left our books at home.
   (b) Amy had fish sandwiches for lunch.
   (c) The goat ate my homework.
2. My mum said my room looked liked a rubbish tip. She said I must clean it. I pushed everything under the bed. Now it looks OK.
3. *Mum says ...*

> Mum says I must keep things neat.
> Mum says I should wipe my feet.
> Mum says I should comb my hair.
> Mum says it is rude to stare.
> Mum says I should work at school.
> Mum says I should never drool.
> Mum says I should eat good food.
> Mum says I should not be rude.
>
> Mum says I should clean my nails.
> Mum says I should not tell tales.
> Mum says I should be polite.
> Mum says I should never bite.
> Mum says I should exercise.
> Mum says I should not tell lies.
> Mum says I should do more walking.
> I think Mum should do less talking.

Additional activities

Pupils can:

1. Read part of the class reader and take note of full stops and capital letters. Pupils try reading it as if it didn't have punctuation and note the difference.
2. Take turns writing a full sentence on the board on a given topic.
3. Write a class story with each pupil contributing one sentence to the story. The pupils write each full sentence as they go.
4. Write a list of things a parent tells them they may or may not do. Correct punctuation must be used.

Recommended reading:

The pupils can read poems with simple punctuation; e.g.
Two-pants Turner by Angie Turner

Capital letters and full stops help make sense of what we read.

1 Add capital letters and full stops to these sentences.

(a) our teacher left our books at home

(b) amy had fish sandwiches for lunch

(c) the goat ate my homework

> **Full stops are part of punctuation.**

3 Read this poem with your class. Add capital letters and full stops. Read the poem as you add them.

2 (a) Try reading this.

> *my mum said my room looked*
>
> *like a rubbish tip she said i must*
>
> *clean it i pushed everything*
>
> *under the bed now it looks OK*

(b) Add capital letters and full stops. Read it again!

(c) Which was easier to read?

1st ☐

2nd ☐

WHY?

> ### *Mum says ...*
>
> *mum says I must keep things neat*
>
> *mum says I should wipe my feet*
>
> *mum says I should comb my hair*
>
> *mum says it is rude to stare*
>
> *mum says I should work at school*
>
> *mum says I should never drool*
>
> *mum says I should eat good food*
>
> *mum says I should not be rude*
>
> *mum says I should clean my nails*
>
> *mum says I should not tell tales*
>
> *mum says I should be polite*
>
> *mum says I should never bite*
>
> *mum says I should exercise*
>
> *mum says I should not tell lies*
>
> *mum says I should do more walking*
>
> *i think mum should do less talking*

Words you know

Objective

Recognise patterns in words

Activities covered

- Reading a note
- Writing words, focusing on spelling patterns

Background information

This lesson uses words that the pupils should be familiar with. The idea of the lesson is for the pupils to recognise similarities in words, and to get used to different spelling strings and patterns.

Before the lesson

Prepare suitable short texts for the class to view at the start of the lesson. Ask the pupils questions, drawing their attention to similarities and differences in the spelling of words.

The pupils can give examples of how words are similar in a number of ways; e.g. book – rhyming words could be 'look', 'took', 'shook', words that end with k, words that have a double o – 'soon', 'moon', 'foot' and so on.

The lesson

1. Read through the prepared short texts with the class. Ask the pupils questions about the words, making them aware of similarities and differences in the spelling of words.
2. The pupils read the note in Question 1.
3. The pupils complete Question 2. The exercise may be completed as a class or individually. If done individually, go through the questions with the pupils. Answers will not be found in the text.

Answers

1. Teacher check
2. (a) not
    (b) Answers may include – rhyming words: rust, must, crust, dust, gust; fluster; other words that end with st or words that begin with j.
    (c) Answers may include jump, junk, jug, June
    (d) Answers may include bay, bray, clay, day, fray, hay, lay, may, pay, ray, they, way, grey, play, stay, slay, tray
    (e) will not
    (f) Teacher check
    (g) Answers may include ouch, about, south, mouth etc.

Additional activity

Pupils read a poem and write words that are similar in some way to chosen words in the poem.

Recommended reading:

sight words, high-frequency words

1 Read this note.

> Dear Miss Zeeb,
>
> This is a note, just to say,
>
> I will not be at school today.
>
> The sun is out, the skies are blue,
>
> Don't miss me, I won't miss you.
>
> From Andy

> You should only be absent from school if you have a good reason!

2 Read the clues and write the words.

(a) What word do I get if I take the 'e' out of **note**?

_____

(b) Write three words that are similar to **just**.

_____

(c) Write two words that start with **ju**.

_____

(d) Write three words that rhyme with **say**.

_____

(e) don't = do + not. What is **won't**? (Be careful – this is tricky!)

_____

(f) Write one word that rhymes with **blue**. Does it have the same spelling pattern?

_____

(g) Write two words that have the **ou** sound as in the word 'out'.

_____

Spell it out

Objective

Identify and correct spelling errors in a poem

Activities covered

• Writing words
• Discussing words
• Reading a poem
• Correcting mistakes
• Rating the poem

Background information

Pupils should at least be encouraged to try to spell a word they don't know. The teacher should tell the pupils to think of a word that could be similar and apply the same rule. Although it won't always work, it is a starting point. The pupils should not feel afraid to experiment with spelling unknown words.

Before the lesson

The teacher can have his/her own list of words for the pupils to write (see 'Answers' for an example).

The lesson

1. The teacher reads words and the pupils write them on the back of the sheet.
2. The pupils discuss their spellings with the class and correct any they got wrong. The teacher can use other examples of words that have the same spelling rule.
3. The teacher reads the poem **Spelling blooz** to the class.
4. The pupils circle all the mistakes they can find and correct as many as possible, guessing the spellings if they are not sure.
5. The pupils give the poem a score out of ten.
6. All mistakes in the poem are discussed as a class. The teacher should be pointing out spelling rules and patterns and giving examples of similar words. (Not all mistakes can be thoroughly explored as there are too many of them!)

Answers

1. Examples of words: spaceship, kneecap, geography, whistle, earth etc. Words should be relevant to the pupil's learning and should be a little difficult.
2. Teacher check
3. teecha – teacher (**ea** – preacher, peach, beach, reach; **er** – baker, cooker, ladder)
   tink – think (**ink** – blink, sink, wink, rink, link, pink; **th** – throw, thing, thin)
   rite – right (**ight** – light, sight, might, fight, tight, night)
   theez – these
   pirfict – perfect
   wirds – words
   hav – have (**magic e** – gave, pave, grave, wave)
   eyesite – eyesight (**ight** – as before – rite/right)
   wen – when (**wh** – white, where, what, whale)
   right – write

   storee – story (**y as ee** – fairy, Mary, scary, happy, honey)
   brite – bright (**ight** – as before)
   scribels – scribbles (**ibbles** – nibbles, dribbles)
   givs – gives (**magic e** – as before)
   won – one
   mee – me
   rong – wrong (**silent w** – write, wreck, wren)
   cos – because
   kant – can't
   goin – going
   specticils – spectacles
   sea – see
   bootiful – beautiful
   wil – will (**double l** – will, kill, Bill, still, mill, ball, call)

Additional activities

Pupils can:

1. Experience regular dictation exercises.
2. Spell difficult words for fun, such as hippopotamus.
3. Play spelling games, where the teacher gives a word and in groups, pupils must spell it out. Pupils write the spelling on the board, and keep going until the word is spelt correctly. The teacher then points out various spelling patterns and rules.

We don't always spell words correctly. If you don't know how to spell a word, guess!

1 Your teacher is going to read some words to you. Write them down.

2 Discuss the words with your class. Correct any you got wrong.

3 Read this poem. In red pen, circle the mistakes and correct it as your teacher would.

_____

_____

_____

_____

_____

_____

_____

_____

_____

_____

_____

_____

4 Give the poem a score out of 10. [ ]

Spelling Blooz

The teecha says my spellings bad,
But I don't tink she's rite.
Look at all theez pirfict wirds,
She must hav poor eyesite.

Wen I right a storee,
She takes her brite red pen,
And scribels over all my wirds,
And givs me won out of ten.

Wen we hav a spelling test,
She always glares at mee.
She tinks all my wirds are rong,
But that's cos she kant see!

I'm goin to buy her specticils,
So she can see my work.
She'll sea my spellings are bootiful,
And wil feel just like a jerk.

I love my
teddy bare!

Spell it well

Objective

Recognise patterns in words and correct spelling errors

Activities covered

- Reading rhyme
- Finding similar words
- Circling letter patterns
- Correcting spelling errors

Background information

The pupils are working with words in this lesson, and finding similarities between the spelling or sounds of words. It can be any similarities that they find, such as sounds, endings of words, rhyming words, letter strings, patterns etc.

Before the lesson

The teacher can have a list of words and the pupils must think of similar words, looking at different parts of the word; e.g. cat – rhymes with sat, mat, flat etc., cat is similar to cot, cut, (different vowels), or cat is similar to car (same two beginning letters).

The lesson

1. The teacher gives the pupils a list of words, and the pupils think of words that are similar in some way. The teacher needs to guide the pupils in looking at different parts of the word, and finding similarities for the different parts. Make sure that pupils are familiar with the word '***similar***'.
2. The pupils read the given rhyme.
3. The pupils find words in the poem that are similar to words in the list.
4. The pupils circle the parts of the words that are similar.
5. The pupils correct mistakes in the given rhyme and rewrite the rhyme correctly.

Answers

1. Teacher check
2. (a) kettle – little (both have ***ttle*** sound) (b) ship – share (both start with ***sh***)   (c) same – came (both have ***ame***)
   (d) call – all (both contain ***all***)   (e) team – eating/beans/jeans (all have ***ea*** sound) (f) pear – bear (rhyming)
   (g) sad – sat (both start with ***sa***)   (h) stand – and (rhyming)
3. Teacher check
4. Little Miss Muffet, sat on her tuffet, eating her curds and whey. Along came a spider, who sat down beside her, and frightened Miss Muffet away.

Additional activities

Pupils can:

1. Have a constant display of new words in the classroom which gets changed regularly. In this way, pupils can refer to the words when doing a writing task.
2. Keep personal dictionaries with a list of their own words. New words learned in reading can be displayed and discussed from time to time. This could be called a 'Word Wall'.
3. Be given a few words and they must write one word similar to each, saying what the similarities are.

1 Read the rhyme. The words in the list are similar to words in the poem. They will have the same letter patterns.

2 Match the words from the poem to words in the list with similar patterns.

Little Miss Grouch
Sat on her couch,
Eating bacon and beans.
Along came a bear,
Who wanted a share,
Miss Grouch spilt it all on her jeans.

kettle

ship

same

call

team

pear

sad

stand

3 Circle the parts of the word that are similar.

4 All the highlighted words in this rhyme are spelt incorrectly! Rewrite the rhyme correctly.

Litle Mis Muffet,

sat on **he** tuffet,

eeting her curds and whey.

Aloong cam a spider,

hoo sat **donw** beside her,

and frightened **Mis** Muffet **awa**.

_____

_____

_____

_____

_____

_____

If

Objective

Choose topics for writing after conferring with the teacher

Activities covered

- Reading an example of a poem
- Deciding on a writing topic
- Conferring with teacher
- Writing a poem

Background information

This lesson asks pupils to choose their own topic for writing, although they have to start with 'If ...'. Pupils should be given time to think about their topic and ideas can be jotted down. Pupils must then confer with the teacher, discussing their topic and possible ideas. Pupils should not be discussing their ideas with anyone else. The teacher can guide pupils and suggest improvements and commend good ideas. Discussing their work with the teacher will, hopefully, make pupils more confident in their writing task.

Before the lesson

Make available enough time to confer with each pupil on their topic.

The lesson

1. The teacher explains to the class what the lesson is about.
2. The class reads the poem, *Invisible*. The teacher can discuss difficult words such as 'raid', 'wads', 'comfy'.
3. Pupils think about their topic and note ideas. Full sentences are not required here. Some ideas could be: If I was a wizard/teacher/rock star/cat/tree etc.
4. Each pupil confers with the teacher, who praises good ideas as well as suggesting improvements.
5. Pupils write their own poem on a separate sheet of paper. Rhyming is not necessary and the poem can be any length the teacher chooses.
6. The teacher could write a suggested layout on the board:
   If I was.......................
   I would ....
   I would ....
   I would........................ etc.
7. Pupils can read their poems to the class.
8. All poems can be displayed.

Answers

1.–4. Teacher check

Additional activity

Pupils can:

Confer with the teacher when writing letters, stories, poems, fiction, projects etc.

1 Read the poem.

Invisible

*If I were invisible, I'd raid the biscuit tin,
I would get all the vegetables and throw them in the bin.*

*I would hide green, slimy frogs in my sister's bed,
I would take her brush and make-up and hide them in the shed.*

*I would put some drawing pins on the bully's chair,
I would stick wads of bubblegum in his dirty hair.*

*I would run around in knickers, all through the town,
I would go to school in slippers and my very comfy gown.*

*At quarter to ten in the morning, I would ring the hometime bell,
I want to be invisible! Does anyone know the spell?*

2 If you could be anyone or anything for a day what would you be?

_____

_____

3 Write some ideas of things that you would do.

4 Talk to your teacher about your ideas. Once you are ready, write your ideas in a poem on a separate sheet of paper. Start your poem with: 'If ...

Row your boat

Objective

Write new words for a song

Activities covered

- Singing original song
- Singing versions of song
- Changing original words
- Singing songs in music class

Background information

Pupils should write for different audiences, such as a friend, a family member, a pen pal, a visitor to the school, an author, an artist etc. Pupils should be encouraged to complete writing activities for themselves so they see that writing is an important part of everyday life and not just for school! In this lesson, the rhythm of the poems/songs is important and pupils should try to copy this. They can beat out the rhythm on the desk, or even sing it.

Before the lesson

The teacher can have other songs/rhymes for the pupils to change.

The lesson

1. Pupils sing **Row your boat** together as a class.
2. Pupils sing different words to the same song.
3. Pupils change the words of **Row your boat** and write them down.
4. Pupils assess their song.
5. Pupils sing **On top of Old Smokey**.
6. Pupils sing the example on the sheet.
7. Pupils draw a picture to go with the song.
8. Pupils take their versions of the song to music class where the class can sing many of the pupils' versions. (If there is time, pupils can change words to **On top of Old Smokey** too.)

Answers

1.– 2. Teacher check

3. Example:

    Work, work, work at school,
    Each and every day,
    Constantly, constantly, constantly, constantly,
    Teachers have their way.

4.–7. Teacher check

Example: The pupils could start with: On top of spaghetti, On top of potatoes, On top of my poodle, On top of my milkshake, On top of a mountain, On top of the island etc.

(Original, first verse:

On top of Old Smokey,
All covered with snow,
I lost my true lover,
For courting too slow.)

Additional activities

Pupils can:

1. Write letters to different people, such as the local council, a famous person, a family member, a friend or Santa.
2. Write instructions for the pet-sitter.
3. Do everyday writing tasks such as lists, a diary, a timetable, an itinerary, an email, a message or an envelope.
4. Use the same song and write words to do with family.

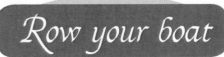

1 Sing the song *Row your boat* as a class!

2 Sing the new words below to the same tune:

> *Laugh, laugh, laugh a lot,*
> *It will keep you sane,*
> *Ha ha ha! Ha ha ha! Ha ha ha! Ha ha ha!*
> *Don't even mind the rain.*

3 Write some new words for the song. | Try to keep the rhythm the same!

_____

_____

_____

_____

4 How well did you do? Give yourself a score out of 5. (5 is the best!) ☐

5 Sing the song *On top of Old Smokey*.

6 Sing the changed words for the song. Draw a matching picture.

> *On top of my wardrobe,*
> *All covered in dust,*
> *I found half a pizza,*
> *And mouldy bread crust.*

7 Take your new songs to your teacher and arrange to sing some of them in class.

Colours

Objective

Decide whether or not to redraft a piece of writing

Activities covered

- Reading a poem about colour
- Writing what the writer thinks about
- Choosing a colour to write about
- Writing about a chosen colour
- Checking own work
- Redrafting if necessary

Background information

Pupils will sometimes have to decide for themselves whether or not to redraft a piece of writing. They should get into the habit of always checking their work and time should be specifically allocated for this. Once the pupils have checked their work, they should make the necessary corrections.

Websites:

(colours)
<http://en.wiktionary.org/wiki/wiktionary_Appendix:Colours>
<www.main.cz/colors/color_names.htm>

Before the lesson

Prepare a list of different colours.

The lesson

1. The class discusses colours. Use the prepared list to introduce various common and uncommon colours.
2. As a class, read through the poem *Silver*.
3. The pupils write three things the writer was thinking of.
4. The pupils choose their own colour to write a poem about and list words they associate with the colour (on a separate page).
5. The pupils use their lists to write a poem about their chosen colour. Each line should start with their chosen colour, as in the example. Rhyming is not necessary.
6. The pupils read through their own work and check it. They redraft if necessary.
7. When the pupils are satisfied with the end result, they can write their poems neatly/type them and display them in the classroom.

Answers

1.– 4. Teacher check

Additional activity

Pupils can:

Check and redraft all writing tasks so that the end result is the best work possible.

Homework suggestion

Make a list of items of a specified colour that can be found at home.

1 Read about this colour.

Silver

Silver is a dentist's cold, unfriendly tool,

Silver is the feeling of touching something cool,

Silver is the fish as it flashes by,

Silver is the streetlight standing proud and high,

Silver is the ocean on a cloudy, gloomy day,

Silver is the sportscar speeding on its way,

Silver is an unbending piece of solid steel,

Silver is the iciness of the sadness you feel,

Silver is fancy dinners of the very rich,

Silver is the wand of a friendly happy witch.

Did you know?
'Grizzle' is a grey colour!

2 Write three things that the colour silver makes the writer think of.

_____

_____

_____

3 Choose your own colour to write about. List words it makes you think of on a separate sheet of paper. Include objects of this colour and feelings.

4 Use your words to write your poem in this space below. Start each sentence with the colour.

Check your work and redraft if necessary!

Looking good

Objective

Confer with the teacher and others on quality of presentation

Activities covered

- Filling in words to complete the poem
- Decorating a poem
- Showing work to others
- Receiving comments/suggestions

Background information

In this lesson, the pupils get feedback from a small group as to what their poem is like and how it is presented. The aim is for the pupils to receive suggestions from their peers as to how their work could be improved. Stress to the pupils that they need to be kind to each other, making positive suggestions and not negative criticisms. (Give the pupils ideas for how a suggestion may begin; e.g. 'Maybe you could ...') It is up to the pupil whether to take the advice or not. The pupils should then be given a chance to improve on their poem. Taking suggestions from the teacher and/or peers can mean that a pupil's work has fewer of mistakes, since it has been redrafted. The pupils will feel better about their work when it looks good. No discussion should take place while the pupils are working on their task.

Before the lesson

The class should be divided into small groups.

The lesson

1. Read the text at the top of the page with the class.
2. Read the poem with the pupils, as it is.
3. The pupils complete the poem. This must be done on their own, although the teacher can read the poem through.
4. The pupils decorate the poem and add an appropriate illustration.
5. The pupils read their poem to their group and show how they have decorated it.
6. The group members give each other suggestions for how their poem and decoration could be improved.

Answers

1. Teacher check; for example:

   Poor **little** bird, just sitting there,

   In your **cage**, no-one to **care**.

   I am feeling **sorry** for you,

   What is it that I can **do**?

   You have no **life**, you're all alone,

   And you don't grumble, you don't **moan**.

   You are colourful, **pretty** and **sweet**,

   But I don't hear you **sing** or tweet.

   It's time to **go**, this is your day,

   The **door** is open, so fly **away**.

2.–4. Teacher check

Additional activity

Pupils can:

Confer with peers and teacher when writing paragraphs, sentences, letters – or just about anything.

Homework suggestion

Show their poem to a family member and ask for feedback on it.

Looking good

Sometimes other people can help us
with our work, by giving suggestions.

> **The African ostrich is**
> **the largest living bird.**

1 Complete this poem. Try to make the two lines rhyme each time.

> Poor _____ bird, just sitting there,
>
> In your _____, no-one to _____.
>
> I am feeling _____ for you,
>
> What is it that I can _____?
>
> You have no _____, you're all alone,
>
> And you don't grumble, you don't _____.
>
> You are colourful, _____ and _____,
>
> But I don't hear you _____ or tweet.
>
> It's time to _____, this is your day,
>
> The _____ is open, so fly _____.

2 Decorate the poem as best you can.

3 In small groups, show each other your work and read your poems. The group
must say what they think of your poem and presentation.

> **Be kind to**
> **each other!**

4 Write one thing they said.

_____

A message for you

Objective

Write notes and messages to different audiences

Activities covered

- Reading a message poem
- Circling important information
- Writing a shortened message
- Writing messages

Background information

Pupils need to realise that writing is not just for school but is used in their everyday lives; e.g. letters, messages, lists, cards, email. Pupils also need to be aware that different tones are needed for different situations; e.g. a letter to a friend will be very different from one to the teacher. Pupils should be aware of their audience *before* they start writing so the right tone can be set. Messages should be precise and to the point, without unnecessary details.

Before the lesson

Examples of how writing is used in our everyday lives could be shown to the class.

The lesson

1. Read the poem *Message* as a class.
2. The pupils circle the words or phrases they think are important, and rewrite the message in shortened form. Full sentences are not necessary.
3. The pupils write a different message.

Answers

1. Teacher check
2. Ryan's, shop, football pitch, Grandma's house, Tommy Grill's, Uncle Sam's, Killian Po
3.–4. Teacher check

Additional activities

Pupils can:

1. Write a letter to a friend or family member and post it or give it to the addressee.
2. Write a message to the teacher to explain an absence from school.
3. Write thank you notes.
4. Write letters of apology.
5. Practise writing messages that tell family members where the pupils are.

Sometimes we need to write messages. Messages need not be long but must have the most important facts.

> **You should always leave a message if you are going somewhere!**

1 Read this long message.

Message

Mum, this is a message to let you know,
I've a few things to do, and I've got to go.
I'll be going to Ryan's to fix his bike,
Then we'll be walking to the shop with Mike.
I'll be stopping off at the football pitch,
To do some training with Ben and Mitch.
I'll be dropping by at Grandma's house,
She wants me to get rid of a pesky mouse.
I'll be heading then to Tommy's Grill,
To have some burgers with Carol and Jill.
I'll be making my way to Uncle Sam's,
Whose mommy sheep has had two lambs.
Then I'll be visiting Killian Po,
We're doing a project called 'My Big Toe'.
I'll try not to be long, I won't be too late,
As I have to get ready to go out with Kate.

2 Circle the words or phrases you think are important.

3 Write the message in shortened form.

> **Messages don't need full sentences!**

4 Write this message.

The teacher asks you to write a message to the headteacher,
asking him/her to come and speak to your naughty class.

_____

_____

Trouser hunt

Objective

Read and discuss a narrative poem and answer questions about it

Activities covered

- Reading a poem as a group
- Discussing a poem
- Answering questions

Background information

This lesson focuses on looking at a process. Tell the pupils that the order of the process of looking for the trousers is important. Other processes can be discussed too, such as making a meal ('What would happen if I cooked the carrots first and then peeled them?'), getting ready for school ('What would happen if I got dressed and then stepped into the shower?'), the school day ('What would happen if we had lunch break first thing in the morning?') etc. The pupils can also provide other examples of when order in a process is important.

Recommended reading:

Dinner on Elm Street by Michaela Morgan

Websites:

<www.fieldmuseum.org/Chocolate/making.html> (for chocolate making)

<http://home.howstuffworks.com> (for the teacher)

<http://walkers.corpex.com/cr15p5/crisps.asp> (how crisps are made)

Before the lesson

The class should be divided into groups.

Provide other examples of processes to discuss with the class.

The lesson

1. Discuss with the pupils the importance of order in certain processes.
2. Discuss the more difficult words or phrases in the poem, such as 'searched', 'vanished without a trace' etc.
3. Read the poem ***Trouser hunt*** in groups and discuss it.
4. In small groups, the pupils answer Question 2.

Answers

1. Teacher check
2. (a) wardrobes, bedroom door, clothing on floor, dresser drawers, duvet, blind, bed, loo
   (b) Messy, because all the clothes are lying on the floor.
   (c) clothes on the floor, doors open, drawers open, bed unmade, stuff lying everywhere

Additional activities

Pupils can:

1. Describe a favourite TV character, and have a partner guess who it is by asking questions.
2. Describe a favourite meal.
3. Tell a story—e.g. a fairytale—to a group.
4. Do simple demonstrations; e.g. how to tie up hair, sew on a button, tie a shoelace, brush their teeth, cover a book. The class can ask questions.
5. In groups, describe their bedroom while members of the group draw it. The group can ask questions. Finished pictures can be compared.

Sometimes lost things can be found in the simplest places!

1 Read this poem with a small group.

Trouser hunt

I can't seem to find my trousers,
  I've looked in every place.
I've searched my entire room,
They've vanished without trace.

I looked in all the wardrobes,
And behind the bedroom door.
I went through all the clothing,
That was lying on the floor.

I checked through all the dresser drawers,
  And under the duvet too.
Behind the blind, and under the bed,
  And even in the loo!

I've turned everything upside down,
  Where on earth could they be?
Now I see them! There they are!
  My trousers are on me!

2 Talk about the poem and answer these questions in your group.

(a) List, in order, all the places in the bedroom the poet looked.

(b) Do you think the poet is a messy or neat person? Say why.

(c) Describe what the poet's room might have looked like when the search was over.

What happened to you?

Teachers notes

Objective

Ask and answer questions about poems and experiences

Activities covered

- Reading a poem
- Discussing a poem as a group
- Devising questions and answering them
- Telling a group about an experience
- Answering questions about an experience
- Asking a speaker questions

Background information

In listening to other pupils' experiences, the pupils will, hopefully, learn to empathise with others in various situations, as well as learn from the experiences of others. In this lesson, the pupils will have to ask questions about the experiences of others, so they will have to listen carefully. When devising questions, the pupils should consider how the speaker might have felt about the experience.

Recommended reading:
(about experiences)

I'm the youngest in my house
by Michael Rosen

Nightmare by Michael Rosen

Our teacher is really from outer space by David Harmer

Before the lesson

The class should be divided into small groups.

The lesson

1. Read the poem **Bathtime** with the class. No class discussion should take place.
2. Discuss more difficult words with the pupils, such as 'barmy', 'oxygen mask', 'detergent', 'dial' and 'frocks'.
3. In small groups, the pupils discuss the poem and what it may feel like to have the poet's experience.
4. As a group, the pupils devise two questions they might ask the poet, then answer their own questions. Full sentences are not necessary.
5. Each pupil in the group takes a turn to tell the group about an experience they have had.
6. The group must listen carefully and ask the speaker questions about the experience, and how he/she felt.

Answers

1.–2. Teacher check

3. Possible questions and answers may include the following:
   (a) Were you able to breathe? Answer: Yes, I had an oxygen mask.
   (b) Did the machine spin very fast? Answer: Yes, I felt quite dizzy at times.
   (c) Were you still dirty afterwards? Answer: No, I was spotlessly clean.
   (d) What did it feel like? Answer: It felt like a scary ride at a funfair.

4. Teacher check

Additional activity

Pupils can:

Prepare a talk on one of the following topics: 'A scary time in my life', 'Dinner at my house', 'A time I'll never forget', 'The best birthday', 'It really hurt!', 'I wish I had not done that!', 'What a day!'. The class can ask questions after the talk is complete.

Homework suggestion

Tell their family about an experience they have had at school. The family member(s) must ask questions.

86 Poetry skills

Prim-Ed Publishing® ~ www.prim-ed.com

We have all had good and bad experiences.

1 Read the poem as a class.

Bathtime

My mother went and bought,
a very big white machine.
This was not the usual kind,
*it was to make **kids** clean.*

'Put on your mask and get inside',
said my mother very calmly.
I really felt quite terrified,
I thought that she'd gone barmy!

I put on the oxygen mask,
this was to give me air.
I thought, 'This is just crazy!'
But to moan I didn't dare.

Mum placed me right inside the tub,
She had a huge big smile.
She threw in some detergent,
and then she flicked the dial.

The machine went spinning round and round,
it really was quite fun.
I gurgled, splashed and sploshed about,
until the wash was done.

'You smell so beautifully fresh!' she said,
and tossed me in with her frocks,
and hung me on the washing line,
among the shirts and socks.

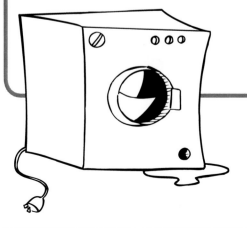

2 In a small group, discuss the poem and what it may feel like to be washed in this way. Write four key words from your discussion.

_____

_____

3 As a group, think of two questions you could ask the poet. Make up the answers.

> **Questions end with a ?**

Q. 1 _____

_____

Answer: _____

_____

_____

Q. 2 _____

_____

Answer: _____

_____

_____

4 Tell the group about an experience you have had. The group must ask you questions about it.

Question time

Objective

Ask questions that will satisfy his/her curiosity and wonder

Activities covered

- Reading a poem aloud as a group
- Asking questions
- Making up answers where no information is available

Background information

Pupils should discuss the given poem in their groups. It's important that they understand the poem before doing group work, so the storyline should be discussed. Pupils should be reminded of the question words: What? Why? When? Who? Where? Which? What if? etc. These can be displayed in the classroom or written on the board. Pupils should always be encouraged to ask questions.

Recommended reading:

(questions)

Who's stuck in the bathroom?
by Steve Turner

Questions, questions by Steve Turner

Before the lesson

The class will be divided into groups.

The teacher should collect some information about a T-Rex to discuss.

The lesson

1. The teacher reads the poem **Friend or foe** with the class. Minimal discussion should occur, as long as pupils understand the storyline.
2. The teacher can discuss more difficult words, such as 'foe', 'rare', 'sneak', 'aware', 'concerned', 'plump', 'selects'.
3. The pupils read the poem and discuss it. As a group, the pupils choose three questions they would like to ask the speaker.
4. The pupils make up answers to their questions.
5. The pupils write a pet name they would give a dinosaur.
6. All questions and answers are discussed as a class, with all groups contributing to the discussion.

Answers

1. Teacher check
2. Possible questions:

   What games do you play together? Where did you meet your friend? Why are you not afraid of him? How does he fit in the shower? What kind of things does he talk about? When did you meet him? Why do you think he wants you to eat a lot? Who else is the T-Rex friends with? etc.
3. Teacher check

Additional activity

Pupils can:

Write 'I wonder why' poems, stating things in life they are curious about, or don't understand.

Homework suggestion

Ask their family members questions about a pet they have had.

*Have you ever had a friend that turned out
to be far from a friend?*

1 Read this poem aloud as a group.

Friend or foe?

*I have a rare and special pet,
    Pooky is his name.
Since he's come into my life,
    it's never been the same.*

*We play together every day,
    we talk for hours and hours.
I have to sneak him in the house
    for him to have his showers.*

*See, Mum is not aware of him,
    she doesn't know he's there.
She'd make me get rid of him,
    and that would not be fair!*

*He's so concerned about my health,
    he says I should eat more.
He says I should be so plump that
    I won't fit through the door.*

*Yes, my friend cares a lot for me
    he says that he selects,
to be with me until the end,
    My friend and pet T-Rex.*

2 If you could meet this person, what would you like to ask him? Write down three questions as a group. Make up the answers if you do not know them.

Q. 1 _____

_____

Answer: _____

_____

_____

Q. 2 _____

_____

Answer: _____

_____

_____

Q. 3 _____

_____

Answer: _____

_____

_____

3 What special 'pet' name would you give to a friend like the one in the poem?

_____

Sea creatures

Objective

Pursue individual interests through independent reading of fiction and nonfiction

Activities covered

- Reading a poem
- Answering questions
- Choosing a topic
- Researching a topic
- Recording information

Background information

Pupils should have easy access to a choice of materials to read. They are far more likely to read if the subject matter interests them. Weaker readers can choose shorter books, with more illustrations. Pupils should have access to a wide range of fiction and nonfiction books either in their school library or local library. For this lesson, the pupils will need to be able to gather information about sea creatures.

Recommended reading:

(about the sea)

The whale's hymn by Brian Patten

The walrus by Michael Flanders

Fishy fashion by David Harmer

Websites:

<www.prekinders.com/ocean_kids.htm>

<www.dltk-kids.com/animals/ocean.html>

Before the lesson

Make sure there is sufficient information for the pupils to access to research a sea creature.

The lesson

1. Read the poem **Walrus snog** with the class.
2. Discuss difficult words from the poem, such as 'handsome', 'moustache', 'snout', 'tiz', 'clam', 'smooch' and 'snog'.
3. The pupils answer the questions about the poem.
4. The pupils discuss interesting sea creatures. Each pupil chooses his/her own sea creature on which to do a mini-project.
5. The pupils research their topic, either at school or for homework. The teacher can read through the questions so the pupils know what information is required. The pupils do not need to go into much detail.
6. The pupils write up their information. The mini-project can then be cut out and displayed in the classroom.

Answers

1. Teacher check
2. (a) 700   (b) to sniff out food   (c) snails, clams or fish
3. Teacher check

Additional activities

Pupils can:

1. Read up on a country they would like to visit and complete a small project/give a talk on it.
2. Look at the websites about 'favourite TV programmes' and then write a passage about them.
3. Read up on an activity/sport that interests them and give a demonstration to the class.
4. Research their chosen sea creature further.

There are so many interesting creatures living in the sea!

1 Read this poem about one of them.

Walrus snog

I know you think I am handsome,
It is my smart moustache, it is.
It is all the hairs upon my snout,
That have you in a tiz.

Up to seven hundred hairs on it,
And I use it to sniff out food,
But if you ask me for a kiss,
I will not think you rude.

My nose sometimes gets food in it,
Like a snail or clam or fish,
But will make the smooch more tasty,
And you will have your wish.

'Snog' is a slang word for kiss!

The walrus is protected from the cold by a thick layer of blubber!

2 Answer these questions.

(a) How many hairs could a walrus have on his nose?

_____

(b) What does he use his hairy nose for?

_____

(c) Name two types of food he eats.

_____

_____

3 Choose your own sea creature, read about it and complete the table below.

Creature	_____
Type of creature	_____
Colour	_____
Size	_____
Where it is found	_____
What it eats	_____
One interesting fact	_____
	_____

Question it

Objective

Adopt an active approach to a text by posing his/her own questions

Activities covered

- Reading a poem as a class
- Formulating questions
- Answering a partner's questions

Background information

Pupils are always answering teachers' questions (hopefully), but they also need an opportunity to devise simple questions themselves. Pupils will need to have a good understanding of a text if they are to formulate questions about it. They should be reminded that questions end with a question mark and often start with who, what, where, when, which, why or how. 'Question words' should be permanently displayed in the classroom.

Recommended reading:

Pupils can read

Where do all the teachers go?
by Peter Dixon

Does the house sleep at night?
by Steve Turner

Do I talk in my sleep? by Steve Turner

Before the lesson

The class should be divided into pairs.

The lesson

1. Remind the pupils about what questions are – what words they might start with and how they end in a question mark. The class can give various examples of questions.
2. Read the poem ***Dressing up*** aloud while the class follows.
3. Discuss more difficult words, such as 'impressing', 'clients', 'necklace', 'amazing', 'impressed' and 'dress sense'.
4. In pairs, the pupils formulate five questions for their partner to answer.
5. The pupils swap pages and answer each other's questions. Answers should be full sentences and not just words. The pupils then check each other's answers and make note of their scores.

Answers

1. Teacher check
2. Answers may include 'What colour is her skirt?' 'Where is the family going?' 'What shape are the earrings?' 'What did she have on her knees?' 'Was her mother pleased?'

Additional activities

Pupils can:

1. Take turns asking and answering questions using a variety of different materials, such as products, instructions, recipes, class timetable, directions, maps, adverts, film line-ups etc.
2. Draw the outfit described in the poem ***Dressing up***. Drawings can be displayed in the classroom with a copy of the poem.

It is your turn to ask the questions!

❶ As a class, read this poem.

Dressing up

'We are going out to dinner,
And I need you to look smart.
Your dad is impressing clients,
Family must play their part.'

Ooooh, I got really excited,
Here was my chance to shine.
I had amazing dress sense,
I knew I could look fine.

On first went my spotty vest,
Then the orange, frilly skirt,
A shiny purple necklace,
And a pink and yellow shirt.

Some silver, shimmering stockings,
And a red and woolly coat,
With big, bright banana buttons,
And a hat shaped like a boat.

And then some clip-on earrings,
That were shaped like Christmas trees,
Some fluffy brown and cosy boots,
And knee pads on my knees.

The final touch, a lilac scarf,
Gold ribbons in my hair,
My mother was just so impressed,
That all she did was stare.

❷ In pairs, read the poem aloud. Write five short questions about the poem for your partner to answer. You will have to swap worksheets!

Questions end with a ?

(a) Question: _____

Answer: _____

(b) Question: _____

Answer: _____

(c) Question: _____

Answer: _____

(d) Question: _____

Answer: _____

(e) Question: _____

Answer: _____

Over the moon

Objective

Develop comprehension strategies

Activities covered

- Reading a poem
- Answering questions
- Describing something that makes him/her happy

Background information

There are many different ways to give pupils practice in comprehension strategies. Poetry is useful because the text can usually be read in one sitting and there can often be different interpretations. Pupils should be developing comprehension strategies with the teacher's guidance; e.g. looking at the words in the questions and finding the same words in the text. All material used for comprehension must be understood before questions can be answered; therefore, it is very important that comprehension exercises are age-appropriate and relevant.

Recommended reading:

Use other poems for comprehension exercises, such as:

Ghosts by Kit Wright

What teacher did on her holiday by Roger Stevens

Before the lesson

A short comprehension exercise could be done together as a class.

The lesson

1. Complete a short comprehension exercise as practice with the class.
2. Read the poem ***Friday afternoon***.
3. Explain more difficult words/phrases in the poem such as 'ruin', 'require a wage', 'remote', 'over the moon'.
4. Pupils discuss how they might feel about Friday afternoons.
5. Read through the questions with the pupils.
6. The pupils answer the questions.
7. The pupils write something that makes them happy, to complete Question 3.

Answers

1. Teacher check
2. (a) Teacher check   (b) false/true/false
   (c) hamster   (d) take a bath
3. Teacher check

Additional activity

Pupils can:

Read various types of text and answer questions on them. Texts that could be used include newspaper articles, adverts, product labels, menus, timetables and comic strips.

We all feel happy at some time.
It's a great feeling!

1 Read this poem.

> There are about 52 Friday afternoons in a year!

Friday afternoon

I don't care what you say to me,
because it's Friday afternoon.
You can call me all sorts of funny names,
this feeling you can't ruin.

You can make me eat cabbage and mince,
I'll even wash my plate.
I'll pretend the mean neighbour,
Is my very bestest mate.

I'll tidy my entire room,
I'll clean the hamster's cage.
If you tell me to, I'll take a bath,
and I don't require a wage.

You can play with all my favourite games,
you can keep the TV's remote.
I'll be kind to my bratty sister,
I'll hang up my winter coat.

Yes, nothing can push me down today,
I could jump right over the moon.
You'll find me willing and cheerful,
on this Friday afternoon.

3 Describe something that makes you really happy.

2 Answer these questions.

(a) How does the poet feel? Why?

_____

_____

_____

(b) Answer true or false.

  (i) The neighbour is his/her best friend.

    ☐ True ☐ False

  (ii) The poet does not like cabbage.

    ☐ True ☐ False

  (iii) The poet gets on well with his/her sister.

    ☐ True ☐ False

(c) What pet does the poet have?

_____

(d) How will the poet get clean?

_____

_____

Alphabet

Objective

Perform alphabetical tasks

Activities covered

- Reading a poem as a class
- Placing words in alphabetical order
- Circling letters, starting with specified letters

Background information

Pupils should know their alphabet but can regularly be given alphabetical tasks for reinforcement.

Before the lesson

Examples of words in alphabetical order could be prepared to introduce the lesson.

The lesson

1. Introduce the lesson using examples of alphabetical order. The pupils should do this alphabetical exercise orally.
2. Read the poem *Tricks* to the class, while the pupils follow.
3. Discuss more difficult words from the poem, such as 'wed', 'fibs', 'sled', 'rare', 'stunts', 'parading'.
4. The pupils place the given words in alphabetical order.
5. The pupils find words that start with letters of the alphabet in the poem. The teacher should stress that this exercise must be done in order. The letters that won't be found are listed. The pupils should do this exercise on their own.
6. The pupils choose five words from the poem and arrange the letters in each word in alphabetical order. The pupils can then try and read the words.

Answers

1. Teacher check
2. circus, donkey, elephant, geese, monkeys, woman
3. Teacher check

Additional activities

Pupils can:

1. List the names of everyone in the class in alphabetical order.
2. Arrange the letters in their first name and last name in alphabetical order. Try and read their new name.
3. Look through simple dictionaries and find words given by the teacher.
4. Put into alphabetical order all the words in a given paragraph.
5. Write an alphabet poem as a class with each letter of the alphabet being used to start a line. The poem could be written by groups in the class with each group getting a few letters.

Homework suggestion

Find objects around the home beginning with each letter of the alphabet. These can be discussed the following day.

1 Read this poem as a class.

Tricks

'Mum, today I saw geese that were coloured bright red!'
'Oh, please stop talking such nonsense, Fred!'

'Mum, today I saw monkeys about to wed!'
'Oh, do stop telling such fibs now, Fred!'

'Mum, today I saw a man nearly stab a woman dead!'
'Oh, I do wish you'd stop all your lying, Fred!'

'Mum, today I saw an elephant pulling a sled!'
'Oh, do tell the truth for once, dear Fred!'

'Mum, today I saw a man with a donkey head!'
'I'm tired of all your rubbish, now go to bed, Fred!'

Then Mum looked out the window,
and what did she see there?

But people dressed quite strangely,
and animals quite rare.

They were practising their acts and stunts,
parading up and down.

Poor Fred was only telling Mum
the circus was in town.

Poor Fred!

2 Place these words from the poem in alphabetical order.

geese	monkeys	woman	elephant	donkey	circus

_____

_____

3 Circle words in the poem that start with each letter of the alphabet. Do them in order! The only letters you won't find are j, k, v, x, z.

Say what you think

Objective

Express a more formal response by giving a considered personal opinion of a poem

Activities covered

- Reading a poem
- Answering questions
- Writing a review

Background information

The questions about the poem will guide the pupils to think about their opinions. When writing reviews, the pupils should, at this age, be given a list of headings to go by; e.g. characters, story. The pupils should be encouraged to speak honestly about the book/ poem; they have a right to dislike something as long as they can give a reason for it.

Before the lesson

An example of a poem could be provided that can be discussed as a class.

The lesson

1. Read the prepared poem to the class. Ask the pupils to say what they think of it and why. Aspects such as story line and characters can be discussed. The word 'characters' may need to be explained.
2. Read the poem *Primary zoo* with the class. No discussion should take place at this time. Explain more difficult words in the poem, such as 'peculiar', 'mild', 'strut', 'venomous' and 'array'.
3. Read through the questions, but do not discuss them.
4. The pupils answer the questions. All questions and answers are then discussed as a class.

Answers

1. Teacher check
2. It's about the different characters that can be found in the classroom.
3. parrots, lemmings, lions, orang-utans, snakes, spiders, cats, porcupines, lambs, mice
4.–5. Teacher check

Additional activities

Pupils can:

1. Write formal reviews on the following: a TV show, a type of cereal, a book they've read, a film, a song etc.
2. Make animals from the poem *Primary zoo* and/or characters in the class, using modelling clay.

1 Read this poem. Think carefully about whether you like it or not and why.

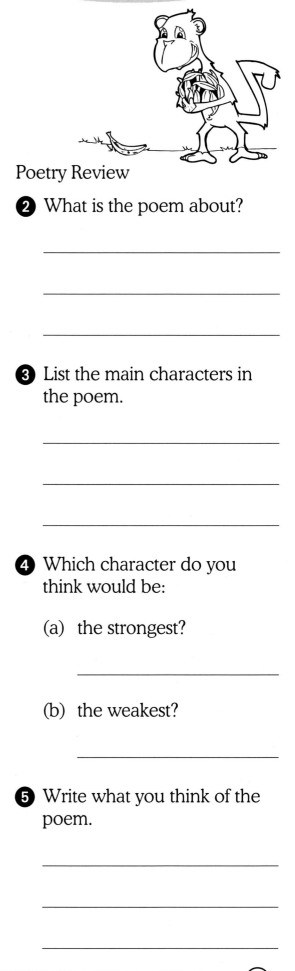

Primary zoo

My classroom is just like the zoo,
With creatures tame and wild.
Some with habits peculiar,
And some with manners mild.

There are the colourful parrots,
And all they do is talk,
And some rather senseless lemmings,
Who don't know pens from chalk!

There's those who strut about like lions,
Kings of the jungle are they,
And hairy big orang-utans,
That simply want to play.

We also have a variety of snakes,
Of the venomous sort.
And an array of spindly spiders,
In whose web you might get caught!

We have some snobby, snooty cats,
Their noses stuck in the air,
And prickly, stickly porcupines,
Of them you must beware!

Thank goodness, there are gentle lambs,
Who never hurt or shout,
And quiet, squeaky little mice,
Who scuttle quietly about.

Yes, our room is quite noisy,
With beasts of every kind.
The zookeeper, Miss Krout, says,
We drive her out her mind!

There was a rhesus monkey in Australia who could drive a tractor!

Poetry Review

2 What is the poem about?

_____

_____

_____

3 List the main characters in the poem.

_____

_____

_____

4 Which character do you think would be:

(a) the strongest?

_____

(b) the weakest?

_____

5 Write what you think of the poem.

_____

_____

_____

Surf the net

Objective

Use information technology to increase motivation to read and to enhance reading development

Activities covered

- Looking up poetry on the Internet
- Answering questions

Background information

It is very important that pupils are taught Internet safety and this is the perfect lesson to introduce it. Pupils need to be supervised by an adult when on the Internet at school or at home. They must be made aware of the dangers of the Internet and realise that they should never give any personal information about themselves to strangers, not even their names. Schools should have a policy on Internet safety.

Before the lesson

Find one or more websites featuring children's poetry. (See suggested websites at the bottom of this page.)

The lesson

1. Discuss with the pupils the concept and importance of Internet safety.
2. Read through the questions with the pupils so they are aware of what they are looking for.
3. The pupils look at poetry websites. The teacher can assist and show pupils how to type an address (URL) if they don't already know. Pupils can take turns with this task, depending on how many computers the school has. While the pupils are on the Internet, others in the class can either answer the questions or complete other language tasks.
4. The sites can be discussed as a class—the best sites, the most interesting, the most information etc.

Answers

1.–7. Teacher check

Additional activity

Pupils can:

Use the Internet for many aspects of language; e.g. online grammar games, stories, plays, reading other children's work, language workshops, worksheets for reinforcement.

Websites:

These are suggested poetry sites for the pupils to look at.

<www.magneticpoetry.com/kidspoetry>

<www.poetry4kids.com>

<www.gigglepoetry.com>

<www.fizzyfunnyfuzzy.com>

The Internet has a lot of information. Always make sure you check with an adult before going on the Internet.

Find a poetry website and answer these questions.

> **www stands for 'World Wide Web'**

1 Write the URL (the website 'address') here.

www. _____

2 What is the website called?

_____

3 How many pages are there?

_____

4 Are there any pictures or photos? Describe one.

_____

_____

_____

5 Do you think the website is interesting? ☐ yes ☐ no

Say why.

_____

_____

6 Read some of the poems on the website. Decide on a favourite.

7 Write the title of your favourite poem and name its author.

_____

_____

You are invited

Objective

Write in a variety of genres

Activities covered

- Reading an invitation poem
- Answering questions
- Writing an invitation in draft form
- Writing an invitation neatly

Background information

Pupils should enjoy writing an invitation because it should be something most of them can relate to. The teacher should keep writing activities varied and relevant.

Recommended reading:

Before the pupils can write in a variety of genres, they need to read different types of material.

Websites:

(ideas for writing – teachers)

<www.proteacher.com/070038.shtml>

<www.abcteach.com>

<www.teachingideas.co.uk/english/contents.htm>

<www.primaryresources.co.uk/english/english.htm>

<www.enchantedlearning.com>

Before the lesson

Some examples of when we might receive an invitation could be provided. A general invitation format could be written on the board.

The lesson

1. Discuss with the class invitations and when we might receive/send them; for example, birthday parties, weddings, baby showers, engagements, graduations, confirmations, wedding anniversaries, Christmas, house-warmings.
2. Read the invitation poem as a class. Discuss the poem and any details that Paddy left out.
3. The pupils state whether they think they would enjoy the party and why/why not.
4. The pupils write their own invitation, firstly as a draft. The pupils can refer to the example on the board if necessary.
5. The pupils can then confer with the teacher and redraft their work. Once they are happy with it, they can write it neatly or type it out on the computer.
6. All invitations are displayed in the classroom.

Answers

1.–4. Teacher check

Additional activity

Pupils can:

Write captions for photos, notes, Christmas shopping lists, a letter to a fictional character, advertising slogans, posters, door signs, menus, adverts, dialogues, nonfiction etc.

1 Read this birthday invitation as a class.

> Dear Jerry,
>
> You're invited to my birthday,
> It's on the 10th of May,
> I do hope you can make it,
> It will be a real fun day.
>
> There'll be sweets and choc-chip cookies,
> And a giant birthday cake,
> The cost is just ten pounds,
> And you'll also get a shake.
>
> And don't forget my present,
> Please don't buy too cheap,
> So, please come to my party,
> The balloon and hat you keep.
>
> From Paddy
>
> RSVP 1st May

2 Do you think you would enjoy this party? Say why/why not.

_____

_____

_____

_____

_____

3 Write your own invitation to a friend, inviting him/her to a party you are having. Complete your draft below.

4 Improve your invitation. Rewrite it neatly on a separate sheet of paper or card.

Excuses!

Objective

Write a version of a story told by the teacher

Activities covered

- Listening to a narrative poem
- Drawing pictures of each verse
- Writing a poem as a story in own words, using keywords

Background information

The aim of this lesson is for the pupils to retell a story in their own words. In this instance, the pupils can draw pictures next to the verses so they can remember the sequence. The pictures drawn need not be works of art, as long as the pupils know themselves what they have drawn! The poem should be discussed as a class so that the pupils are familiar with it before beginning their writing task. The pupils will be using their listening and summarising skills in summing up the story.

Before the lesson

Prepare some short passages to read to the class. The pupils can then retell them orally.

The lesson

1. Read out the prepared passage to the class and have the pupils retell the story orally.
2. Read the poem **Teacher 1 Pupil 0** to the class while the class follows.
3. The poem and its title are then discussed as a class. More difficult words can also be discussed, such as 'aware', 'cunning', 'assumed', 'criminal', 'arrested'.
4. Pupils read the poem to themselves and draw simple sketches next to each verse to remind themselves of the events.
5. The pupils write their own version of the story using the keywords provided and their pictures to guide them. The pupils should tick the keywords as they use them.

Answers

1.–3. Teacher check

Additional activities

Pupils can:

1. Read various types of texts such as short stories, fairytales, rhymes etc. The pupils retell them in their own words.
2. Watch a TV show or film and retell the story briefly.
3. Read poetry and retell the story; e.g. **The little dog** by Cannon and Ball or **Blow out** by Dave Calder. Any other poems that tell a story would be suitable.

Sorry I didn't finish my homework Sir, but my favourite TV shows were on.

❶ Follow the poem as it is read.

Teacher 1 Pupil 0

'Derek, where is your homework?
Can you tell me why it's not done?
Were you kidnapped last night by a vampire?
Or were you just out having fun?'

'Well, Miss, it was a very hard evening,
And I know you will understand,
There was a huge storm and the lights went out,
We had to eat food that was canned.

Our poor little dog was frightened,
And so he ran away,
I had to go right after him,
In case he lost his way.

I followed him into a darkened field,
Of the bull I was not aware,
He chased us and my clothes got ripped,
I ran home cut and bare.

We were visited then by cunning thieves,
Who were trying to get into our shed,
Mum took out her frying pans,
And hit them over the head.

Somebody must have called the police,
Then Mum was yelling at Dad,
She said he should have stopped the thieves,
Oh boy, but she was mad!

The police arrived with flashing lights,
And saw Mum yelling a lot,
They assumed Dad was the criminal,
And arrested him on the spot.

While all of this was going on,
My small brother started to tire,
The candle was not enough light for him,
So he set the room on fire.

The fire brigade came quickly,
And we were all OK,
We are all lucky to be alive,
It was a frightening day!'

'I won't accept such a silly excuse!
You were doing your homework too late!
You will stay in at break times,
Until it's all up to date!'

Teachers. They always have their way.

❷ Read the poem to yourself. Draw small pictures next to each verse to remind you of the events.

❸ Write the poem as a story in your own words. Use some of the words below. Tick them as you use them.

homework	storm	fire	field	thieves
arrest	Mum	dog	bull	police

Let's go shopping

Objective

Write the significant details about an event or an activity

Activities covered

- Reading and discussing a poem
- Talking about experiences
- Writing about experiences

Background information

Pupils need to be able to decide what the important aspects of an event or activity are to enable them to write a short summary of it. It is helpful if pupils write keywords before they begin their writing task. When the pupils are writing about an event or activity, it should preferably be something they have experienced themselves.

Recommended reading:

(experiences)

Stuck in the middle of the afternoon
by Steve Turner

Our teacher has us worried
by Barry Buckingham

Christmas pudding by Charles Thomson

Two lists by Tony Bradman

Chicken poxed by Valerie Bloom

Nightmare by Michael Rosen

Websites:

(shopping)

<www.harrods.com>

<www.hamleys.com>

Before the lesson

Prepare examples of important details about an event; e.g. someone's party.

The lesson

1. Discuss with the class an activity or event. Ask pupils to explain what the important details are. Write any keywords on the board.
2. The class reads the poem ***A bit short***. The teacher should read while the pupils follow. Discuss any difficult words, such as 'enormous', 'gadget'.
3. The class discuss the story of the poem.
4. The pupils can write keywords.
5. The pupils briefly tell the class or a partner/small group about a shopping experience they have had. The teacher can set a time limit.
6. The pupils can then write about it using full sentences. The teacher can refer to 'question' words to help pupils; e.g. 'When did you go?' 'Where did you go?' 'Why did you go?'.
7. Some of the paragraphs can be read out to the class.

Answers

1.–5. Teacher check

Additional activity

Pupils can:

Write about a range of experiences they have had; e.g. school sports day, a visitor who came to the school, a special occasion they attended, a holiday, a party they attended/held, a place they visited, a day at school.

1 Read about this boy's shopping experience.

A bit short

I had money in my pocket,
And it I was going to spend.
The toyshop was enormous,
I would walk it end to end.

I got myself a trolley,
I felt good and warm inside.
The toys were calling out to me,
Like the ocean at high tide.

I threw in some boxes of Lego™,
And a pack of Geomag™,
A red and shiny Spiderman™ suit,
That came complete with bag.

I added some Star Wars™ figures,
As well as a light-up sword,
Some Homer Simpson™ gadgets,
A helmet and skateboard.

In went puzzles, books and games,
Footballs and a bat,
Remote-controlled cars and bikes,
A five-foot fluffy cat.

I'd finished and I was ready to pay,
So I went up to the till.
The pale shopkeeper looked quite shocked,
And handed me the bill.

Four thousand, six hundred
and ninety-three!
This was quite a large sum!
I looked at the ten pound note in my hand,
'Would a credit card do?? M-u-m!!!!!'

2 Discuss the poem as a class.

3 Write keywords about a shopping experience you have had.

_____

_____

_____

4 Tell the class about a shopping experience you have had.

5 Write about your shopping experience.

_____

_____

_____

_____

_____

_____

_____

Why do you think ...?

Objective

Write an explanation for something

Activities covered

- Writing explanations
- Discussing explanations with the class
- Reading a poem and giving explanation

Background information

In order for pupils to explain something well, they will need to give it some thought. The explanation must make sense. The teacher can tell pupils what an explanation is – describing the reasons for something.

Before the lesson

Prepare examples of when and how we use explanations; e.g. explaining to the doctor how we feel, explaining to a shopkeeper why we are returning goods, explaining why we are home late, explaining why chores are not done, explaining why we have chosen to go to Spain on holiday.

The lesson

1. Discuss explanations with the pupils. Give examples of when we use explanations, and the pupils can do the explaining!
2. The pupils complete Question 1 using full sentences.
3. Read the poem *Fair fare* as a class. Discuss difficult words in the poem, such as 'mayhem', 'dodgem cars', 'fare'.
4. The pupils discuss the poem and then write an explanation to complete Question 4.

Answers

1. (a) Answers may include the following: Our bodies need enough nutrients to stay healthy, we will have more energy, we will be able to do our work better.
   (b) Answers may include the following: to learn, to make friends, to keep out of mischief.
2. –3. Teacher check
4. Answers should indicate that the poet feels sick because he/she has eaten too much junk food and been on too many rides.

Additional activity

Pupils can:

Make up humorous explanations for the following: why the kitchen is so messy, why his/her trousers are ripped, why he/she didn't eat dinner, why there's a sheep in the garden, why the police are looking for them, why the front door is gone, why they did not tidy their room etc.

Recommended reading:

(explanation)

Why I am always going to wear my baseball cap by David Harmer

Sometimes you need to give an explanation for something, like why your homework is not done!

Do not start your sentences with 'because'!

1 Answer these questions. Write two full sentences for each.

(a) Why do you think we should eat three healthy meals a day?

_____

_____

_____

(b) Why do you think children should go to school?

_____

_____

_____

2 Read this poem as a class.

Fair fare

Candyfloss and popcorn,
A large and frosty drink,
Greasy chips and burger,
Milkshakes, thick and pink.

Rollercoaster mayhem,
Bumped on dodgem cars,
Flying in the Ghost Ship,
And then the Shooting Stars.

Trying to eat a hot dog,
While the teacups spin so quick,
Sipping my red slushie,
Oh, why do I feel sick?

3 Why do you think the poet feels sick? Discuss as a class.

4 Write an explanation.

I think he feels sick because

_____

_____

_____

_____

_____

_____

Objective

Write a simple sentence and adds words to extend its meaning

Activities covered

- Adding details to simple sentences
- Adding details to a given poem

Background information

In this lesson, the pupils will be adding details to sentences and a poem. They will need to see examples of how this is done before being able to tackle it themselves. Provide many examples at the beginning of the lesson by putting a simple sentence on the board, and then allowing the pupils to come up with the details; e.g. *The girl jumped* could become:

*The **bold** girl jumped **sky high when the headteacher walked in**.*

The terms 'adjective' and 'adverb' need not be mentioned, but the pupils can be coaxed into adding details by asking questions such as why, how, when, where, what, who etc. These can be displayed in the classroom to remind the pupils what questions to ask so that more details can be given.

Before the lesson

Prepare examples of sentences where details can be added as a class.

The lesson

1. Discuss with the class how adding details makes a simple sentence more interesting; e.g. 'The woman ran'. Ask the class to give more details by asking questions such as: 'Which woman? Why was she running? How fast was she running? Where was she running to?' etc. With the class adding details, the sentence could end up, 'The frightened woman ran quickly down the road as she was being chased by a grizzly bear', or something similar.
2. The pupils add details to the sentences.
3. The pupils add details to the poem.
4. The pupils read the poem with and without the details, and decide which version they like more. They then explain why.

Answers

1. Answers will vary. Examples:
   (a) The wicked, nasty witch nibbled the slimy frog's toes.
   (b) The horrid teacher yelled loudly at the well-behaved class.
3. Teacher check

2. Answers will vary. Example:
   *My **lovable, friendly** pup,*
   In the mornings wakes me up,
   *He loves to eat **raw, cold** fish,*
   In a plate and not a dish.
   *We play **ball** games each day,*
   *We have **great** fun, I must say,*
   *He chews my **smelly, sweaty** shoes,*
   But when I'm sad, it's him I choose.

Additional activities

Pupils can:

1. Write the finished poems out neatly and display them in the classroom. Time can be given for pupils to read each other's work.
2. In pairs, add details to a given statement; e.g. 'I went shopping'. Exaggerate the statement by adding ridiculous details; e.g. 'I went shopping last night with my millionaire uncle and he bought me a watch that cost two million pounds'. These sentences can all be done orally.
3. Look at detailed pictures and write one sentence for each, adding details by getting clues from the picture.
4. As a class, add details to a well-known story.
5. Turn a simple sentence into a short story by asking questions and adding details.
6. Describe objects or people using details.
7. Choose a product and make an advertisement for it by using positive details; e.g. shampoo.

Homework suggestion

Tell their parents about their day at school, adding as many interesting details as possible.

You can make your sentences more interesting!

1 Make these sentences more interesting by adding details.

> **Add details to your own writing!**

(a) The witch nibbled.

_____

_____

(b) The teacher yelled.

_____

_____

2 Add details to this poem to make it more interesting.

> My _____, _____ pup,
>
> In the mornings wakes me up,
>
> He loves to eat _____, _____ fish,
>
> In a plate and not a dish.
>
> We play _____ games each day,
>
> We have _____ fun, I must say,
>
> He chews my _____, _____ shoes,
>
> But when I'm sad, it's him I choose.

3 Read the poem first without the details, and then with the details. Which one do you like better?

☐ 1st   ☐ 2nd

Why?

_____

_____

What would you ask?

Objective

Listen to a story and writes down questions to ask about it

Activities covered

- Reading a poem
- Discussing a culture
- Writing questions to ask about a poem
- Discussing questions

Background information

Pupils should be encouraged to ask questions when listening to a story because it demonstrates they are giving thought to what they have heard.

Before the lesson

Research on Africa or another culture could be undertaken in order to discuss it in class with the pupils.

The lesson

1. Read the poem *Africa's child* as a class.
2. The pupils discuss the culture and how their life is different from the boy's.
3. The pupils write three questions they would like to ask the boy if they met him. The questions must be related to the content of the poem.
4. The pupils complete Question 3. All questions can then be discussed as a class.
5. Further discussion about other cultures can be had if there is time; for example, the pupils could think of ways to help those less fortunate than themselves.

Answers

1.–3. Teacher check

Additional activities

Pupils can:

1. Listen to stories told by the teacher and write questions to ask.
2. Question articles about mysterious occurrences such as the Loch Ness Monster or Yeti.

1 Read this poem about a boy in a poor African country.

Africa's child

My home, a mud hut,
and my garden, just sand,
my view, a red sunset,
staining the land.

My chore, to fetch water,
many, many hours away,
watch out, the wild animals,
at the closing of day.

My toys, a few marbles,
and a battered football,
my clothes, secondhand,
and my shoes, none at all.

My dinner, just porridge,
but it tastes so good,
my friends, almost everyone,
in my neighbourhood.

My life, not so bad,
it's all that I know,
but if they offered me more,
I wouldn't say no.

2 Write two ways in which this boy's life is different from yours.

It is different because

_____

_____

_____

_____

_____

3 If you could meet the boy, what three questions would you ask him?

- _____

  _____

  _____

- _____

  _____

- _____

  _____

  _____

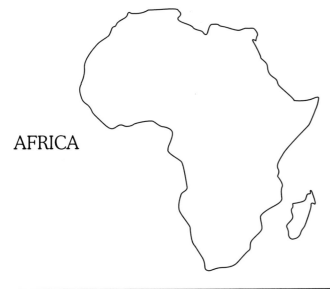

AFRICA

You can help poor children in other countries by donating clothes and toys you no longer need.

Objective

Write and perform action poems

Activities covered

- Reading and performing an action poem
- Writing a four-line action poem as a group
- Performing an action poem as a group
- Assessing a poem
- Putting group poems together and reading as a class

Background information

Pupils should be given the opportunity to read, learn, listen to and recite different types of poetry. The poems should be interesting or funny and should always be about something the pupils can relate to.

Recommended reading:

Poetry anthologies:

Read me and laugh
(poems chosen by Gaby Morgan)

The moon has got his pants on
by Steve Turner

You're not going out like that
(poems chosen by Paul Cookson)

The secret lives of teachers
(poems chosen by Brian Moses)

Utterly brilliant poetry
(edited by Brian Patten)

The day the teacher went batty
by Gervase Phinn

Before the lesson

Some examples of other action poetry could be obtained.

The class should be divided into groups.

The pupils may need a little room to perform the actions in their groups. Practising outside would be the best option if the weather permits.

The lesson

1. Read the action poem as a class without the actions.

2. In small groups, the pupils read the poem and perform the actions. The groups can practise a few times until some fluency is achieved. Actions should all be done together as a group.

3. Still in groups, the pupils make up their own four-line action poem.

4. Groups can practise their poems and then perform them for the class.

5. All the groups' poems are now put together and the class reads each poem in its entirety, adding all the actions.

Answers

1.–5. Teacher check

Additional activities

Pupils can:

1. Read other action poetry, or change well-known poems; e.g. 'If you're happy and you know it ...' can be 'If you're grumpy and you know it, pull a frown' or 'If you're lazy and you know it, say NO WORK' or 'If you're cheerful and you know it, give a laugh (tee hee)' or 'If you're tired and you know it, give a snore'.

2. Read poems in groups and discuss them using questions as guidelines.

3. Recite poetry for the rest of the school or for visitors.

4. Listen to poetry read aloud and then turn the poem into a story.

Homework suggestion

Recite a chosen poem for a family member.

1 In a small group, read the poem and do the actions.

> Stand on your tiptoes,
> Put your hands on the ground,
> Lift your left knee up,
> Then roll your eyes around.
>
> Give yourself a hug,
> Put your right foot on the chair,
> Have a huge big stretch,
> Then gently pull your hair.
>
> Take a little jump,
> Make your face look glum,
> Spin your body round,
> Then twiddle your left thumb.
>
> Put both hands on your elbows,
> Pat your tummy twice,
> Shake somebody's hand,
> And say the teacher's nice!

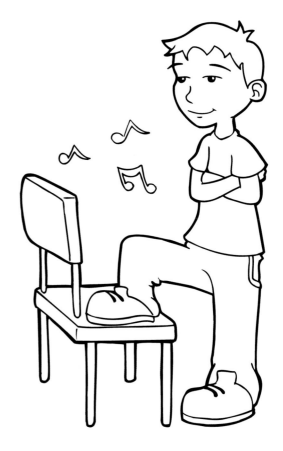

2 In your groups, write a four-line action poem.

_____

_____

_____

_____

3 Practise your poem with the actions. When you are ready, perform it for the class.

4 Rate your action poem.

| **Fantastic** | **Great** | **Good** | **OK** | **Needs work** |

5 Put all the poems together and read them as a class. Do all the actions too!

Teachers notes

Objective

Recreate stories and poems in improvisational drama

Activities covered

- Reading a poem
- Adding actions and acting out a poem as a group
- Performing for the class
- Assessing a performance

Background information

Pupils can use their imagination in acting out stories and poems. Performances need not be too rehearsed, although the pupils should get the opportunity for some practice before performing. Ensure that all pupils are actively involved in their groups.

Before the lesson

Prepare a list of suggestions to help the pupils act out their poem effectively.

The lesson

1. Read the poem **Why?** with the class and then discuss it.
2. The pupils write one thing they don't understand about life.
3. Suggest some ways the pupils might act out the poem.
4. In groups, the pupils decide how they will act out the poem and add actions. Notes can be written on the poem to remind them.
5. The pupils practise the poem and then perform it for the class.
6. The pupils assess their performance.

Answers

1.–6. Teacher check

Additional activity

Pupils can:

Act out poems that tell a story, well-known fairytales and parts of the class reader.

Recommended reading:

Poetry anthologies:

The secret lives of teachers
(poems chosen by Brian Moses)

The works (poems chosen by Brian Moses and Pie Corbett)

Website:

<www.poetryzone.ndirect.co.uk/index2.htm>

1 As a class, read this poem.

WHY?

Why?

I don't understand why
*   I can't punch those boys,*

I don't understand why
*   I can't break my toys.*

I don't understand why
*   I can't roll in the mud,*

I don't understand why
*   My sister hates blood.*

I don't understand why
*   I can't keep this pet snake,*

I don't understand why
*   I can't eat the whole cake.*

I don't understand why
* I can't swing from the lights,*

I don't understand why
*   I can't give Gran frights.*

I don't understand why
*   I can't jump on the table,*

I don't understand why
* I can't shout when I'm able.*

I don't understand why
*   I can't throw my food,*

I don't understand why
*   I can't go to school nude.*

I don't understand why
*   I can't play with a knife,*

But I do understand
That I'm grounded for life!

2 Write one thing you don't understand.

_____

_____

3 In a small group, decide how you will act out this poem. Make notes to show what you plan to do.

> **Make sure everyone is doing something!**

4 Write some actions you will perform.

_____

_____

_____

_____

_____

5 Perform your poem for the class.

6 Rate your performance by colouring the stars.

What nonsense

Objective
Listen to and say nonsense words and unusual words

Activities covered
- Reading nonsense words
- Identifying nonsense words
- Replacing nonsense words with real words
- Making nonsense words

Background information
The pupils will need to draw on their knowledge of sounds when reading nonsense words. For this lesson, all nonsense words rhyme with the intended words. Assistance may be required as some pupils might find this activity difficult. There should be many examples done orally at the start of the lesson, where the pupils are asked to make nonsense words that rhyme with real words. It would be a good lesson to show pupils that rhyming words don't always have the same letter strings or patterns.

Recommended reading:
Parts of poems by Edward Lear

Websites:
(nonsense verse)
<www.answers.com/topic/nonsense-verse>
(for the teacher)
<www.whimsy.org.uk/nonsense.html>

Before the lesson
Prepare lists of words that can be changed into rhyming nonsense words.

The lesson
1. The pupils make nonsense words from the teacher-prepared list.
2. The pupils say the nonsense words in Question 1. This can be done together as a class.
3. Read the nonsense poem to the class while the pupils circle the nonsense words.
4. The pupils replace the nonsense words with words that make sense in context. These should rhyme with the nonsense words.
5. The poem is read again as a class, using the real words.
6. The pupils make rhyming nonsense words out of the list of words given in Question 5.

Answers
1. Teacher check
2. flong, twee, plun, claying, bot, pun, sikes, jall, vaces, zon, geat, flayed, fross
3. ***What's wrong?***

   My three friends and I,
   Have had such good fun,
   We have been playing all day,
   In the hot summer sun.

   We have ridden our bikes,
   And played with a ball,
   We had running races,
   I won them all.

   I beat them at everything,
   We played today,
   Why they are cross with me,
   I just could not say.

4.–5. Teacher check

Additional activities
Pupils can:
1. Change their own names by moving letters.
2. Change place names, cartoon character's names etc. by changing the first letters of each or moving the letters around.

Homework suggestion
Write nonsense sentences about their family. A family member must try to guess what their sentences are.

1 Say these nonsense words.

(a) gloop   (b) fleen   (c) slake

(d) nog   (e) vun   (f) kleesh

(g) chost   (h) glunsh   (i) trilt

(j) broop   (k) snick   (l) zate

2 Circle the nonsense words in the poem.

I zam a kinner.

What's flong?

My twee friends and I,

Have had such good plun,

We have been claying all day,

In the bot summer pun.

We have ridden our sikes,

And played with a jall,

We had running vaces,

And I zon them all.

I geat them at everything,

We flayed today,

Why they are fross with me,

I just could not say.

3 Replace the nonsense words in the poem with rhyming words that make sense. Write them above the nonsense words.

4 Read the poem again with the replaced words.

5 Turn these into nonsense words. Each word should rhyme.

(a) school _____

(b) house _____

(c) cat _____

(d) lunch _____

(e) game _____

(f) time _____

The real words rhyme with the nonsense words!

Clap! Clap!

Objective
Clap the rhythm of poems and rhymes

Activities covered
- Clapping rhymes as a group
- Clapping the rhythm of a poem

Background information
The pupils do not need to learn the word 'syllable' yet but a few examples of clapping words should be done at the beginning of the lesson to show that some words will require more than one clap. The class should do quite a few examples together before the group work begins. Pupils usually have a good feel for rhythm. Stress that rhymes and poems must be read very slowly while clapping out the rhythm. Group work is better for this lesson because the pupils could easily get lost with the rhythm in a class situation. Walk around and check that all groups are on the right track.

Before the lesson
The class should be divided into groups.

The lesson
1. Do some examples together with the pupils, saying words they must clap out; e.g. school, homework, book, naughty, teacher, lunch, dinner, sandwich, beautiful.
2. The pupils clap out the nursery rhyme in small groups, then choose their own rhyme to clap out.
3. The pupils read the poem ***Hometime!*** and clap it out.
4. The pupils clap out their names and count the claps.
5. The whole class claps out the poem together.

Answers
1.–5. Teacher check

Additional activities
Pupils can:
1. Make up their own short rhythm and then put words to it.
2. Listen to a favourite song in class and clap it out.
3. In pairs, have a (slow!) conversation and clap the words out as they say them.
4. Use rhythm boards.

Recommended reading:
Pupils read poems with rhythm; e.g.
Body talk by Benjamin Zephaniah
The music lesson by Clare Bevan
We got rhythm by Mike Jubb

1 In a small group, clap out this nursery rhyme.

Sometimes a word needs more than one clap!

> Little Bo Peep
> Has lost her sheep,
> And doesn't know where to find them.
> Leave them alone, they will come home,
> Wagging their tails behind them.

2 Clap together the rhythm of another nursery rhyme in your groups. Do it a few times if you don't get it right!

3 Clap out this poem.

You will need to read very SLOWLY!

Hometime!

Thank goodness, it is nearly three,
At last I can go home!
I'm watching the seconds tick over,
But I will try to finish this poem.

It has been a long and tiring day,
The teacher was just cruel.
I think I have written a million words,
Oh, why do we have school?

I am watching the big, round clock,
The minute hand is there!
I do have a lot more to say,
But my bottom has left the chair.

Gotta go!!!!!..... Bye!!!!!.....

4 In your groups, take turns to clap out your full name. Say it as you clap. How many claps is it?

5 As a class, clap out the poem as you read it.

That's nonsense!

Objective

Listen to, read, learn and recite more sophisticated nonsense verse and rhyme

Activities covered

- Reading a nonsense poem
- Looking for and underlining nonsense words
- Choosing words from a list

Background information

Reading nonsense words and verse is an excellent way for pupils to practise their phonics. It is something that the pupils usually enjoy doing too. This lesson is slightly more difficult than the previous lesson; therefore, the pupils may require assistance.

Recommended reading:

The Squirdle by Spike Milligan

On the ning nang nong by Spike Milligan

Websites:

<www.nonsenselit.org/Lear> (teacher)

<www.poemhunter.com/edward-lear/poet-6573 >

Before the lesson

Examples of other nonsense verse and rhymes could be chosen to share with the class.

The lesson

1. Read the poem **Duppy dove** as a class.
2. The pupils look for and underline the nonsense words in the poem.
3. The pupils choose words from the list to replace the nonsense words. Tell the pupils that the real words will rhyme with the nonsense words.
4. The pupils reread the poem.

Answers

1.–2. Duppy, dove, nog, flaying, mootball, kitch, zatching, snicks, ganded, fitch, choodle, bittle, bling, blad, kee, ching, nog, flay, choodle, krend, chaw-in-chaw

3. **Puppy love**

    My dog and I were playing,
    Up on the football pitch,
    He was catching sticks I threw,
    One landed in a ditch.

    And there he found a poodle,
    A pretty, little thing,
    She sure was glad to see us,
    And to my hand did cling.

    Now my dog won't play with me,
    He likes the poodle more,
    And I am left without a friend,
    While they sit paw-in-paw.

4. Teacher check

Additional activity

Pupils can:

Write their own nonsense sentences.

1 Read the nonsense poem.

> ### *Duppy dove*
>
> *My nog and I were flaying,*
>
> *Up on the mootball kitch,*
>
> *He was zatching snicks I threw,*
>
> *One ganded in a fitch.*
>
> *And there he found a choodle,*
>
> *A pretty, bittle bling,*
>
> *She sure was blad to kee us,*
>
> *And to my hand did ching.*
>
> *Now my nog won't flay with me,*
>
> *He likes the choodle more,*
>
> *And I am left without a krend,*
>
> *While they sit chaw-in-chaw.*

2 Underline the nonsense words.

3 Write words from the list above the nonsense words in the poem.

poodle	*little*	*friend*
dog	*ditch*	*thing*
play	*football*	*pitch*
paw-in-paw		*love*
cling	*landed*	*catching*
glad	*sticks*	*see*
puppy	*playing*	

4 Read the poem again. Which was easier to read?

☐ Nonsense

☐ Real

Weachers are gooper!

Money matters

Objective

Continue to listen to and enjoy stories and poems being read aloud

Activities covered

- Listening to teacher reading
- Discussing as a class
- Answering questions

Background information

Pupils of all ages love to listen to stories and poems being read aloud to them, as long as they can relate to what's being read. The choice for interesting reading material is endless; the key is to keep it age-appropriate and either exciting or lighthearted if possible. Reading aloud to pupils helps them to practise their listening skills, as well as hearing how the text should be read.

Before the lesson

Other poems could be read aloud to the class.

The lesson

1. Read the poem ***Money matters*** to the pupils while they follow.
2. The poem is discussed and read again if necessary. More difficult words can be explained, such as 'skint', 'laptop', 'cough up', 'grand', 'designer', 'thou', 'shabby', 'decorate', 'plasma screen', 'PSP' (portable playstation).
3. The pupils answer Questions 3–4, using full sentences.
4. All questions and answers are discussed as a class.

Answers

1. Teacher check
2. Answers should include three of the following: laptop, bike, mobile, jeans, bedroom, plasma screen, PSP
3.–4. Teacher check
5. quid, skint, cough up, grand, mates, thou

Additional activity

Pupils can:

Listen to a range of texts read aloud, such as relevant newspaper and magazine articles, humorous and serious poetry, short stories etc.

Homework suggestion

Read the poem to a family member.

Recommended reading:

(poems to enjoy)

The want-want twins by Jackie Kay

Dave Dirt's Christmas presents by Kit Wright

Websites:

\<www.poetry4kids.com\>

\<www.gigglepoetry.com\>

\<www.fizzyfunnyfuzzy.com\>

1 Listen to this poem.

> ### Money matters
>
> *Hey there, Mr Millionaire,*
> *Could you give a few quid to me?*
> *There's a few things I am needing,*
> *And I am skint you see.*
>
> *I could do with a laptop,*
> *That is, if you don't mind.*
> *If you cough up two thousand,*
> *I'll think you very kind.*
>
> *I rather need a mountain bike,*
> *I'm sure you understand,*
> *A young man needs his freedom,*
> *Could you give me five grand?*
>
> *My mobile needs replacing,*
> *There's some mates I need to dial,*
> *Ten grand is what I'll pay you back,*
> *Though it may take a while.*
>
> *I could do with some designer jeans,*
> *Not all that 'cheapy' stuff,*
> *If you give me twenty thou*
> *It should be quite enough.*
>
> *My bedroom is rather shabby,*
> *I need to decorate.*
> *Thirty grand should do the trick,*
> *And I don't think it should wait.*
>
> *But now that I am thinking,*
> *I'm desperate for quite a bit,*
> *I think a hundred thousand,*
> *Should just about cover it.*
>
> *A plasma screen is a definite must,*
> *And of course, a PSP,*
> *On second thoughts, I need the lot,*
> *Could you give it all to me?*
>
> **All that glitters**
> **is not gold.**

'Skint' is a slang word meaning having no money!

2 Discuss with the class the things the poet wants. Write three.

- _____
- _____
- _____

3 Do you think the poet is being reasonable? Say why/why not.

_____
_____
_____

4 What things would you like to buy if you could afford to?

_____
_____
_____
_____

5 Circle the slang words in the poem.

Tongue twisters

Objective

Read and write tongue twisters

Activities covered

- Reading tongue twisters
- Changing letters of words
- Timing a two-line tongue twister
- Writing own tongue twisters

Background information

In order for pupils to remain interested in what they are reading, texts need to be varied and age-appropriate, as well as entertaining. This lesson concentrates on tongue twisters and should be kept lighthearted. The lesson requires whole-class participation.

Ideas for writing a tongue twister:

A. Choose a letter of the alphabet.

Choose a name starting with that letter.

Ask yourself What did he/she do? Where did it take place? When did it happen? Why did it happen?

Answers to these questions should all start with the same letter chosen at the beginning. By the end of it, you should have a tongue twister of sorts!

B. Another idea is to make four lists: nouns/ verbs/adjectives/adverbs – use the same letter for all the words in the list. String the words together to make sentences.

C. Take an existing tongue twister and change the letters used.

Before the lesson

Other examples of tongue twisters could be read to the pupils.

The lesson

1. The pupils read the tongue twister poem. They can read it together as a class a few times.

2. The pupils change all the 'b' words to 'p' words and try to read it again. This can be done orally and the pupils will find this quite difficult. It does not have to be perfectly read! The pupils can underline all the 'b' words beforehand to make it easier.

3. The pupils read a two-line tongue twister and time how fast they can say it.

4. The pupils write their own tongue twister sentence. This must be a full sentence. (See *Background information* for ideas)

5. Some of the tongue twisters from Question 4 can be read as a class.

Answers

1.– 4. Teacher check

Additional activity

Pupils can:

Read a range of texts, including menus, recipes, timetables, articles, newspapers, adverts, invitations, cards, flyers, billboards, road signs, instruction manuals, comics, magazines, film reviews, labels, posters, business cards, web pages etc.

Websites:

(tongue twisters)

<www.indianchild.com/tongue_twisters.htm>

<www.fun-with-words.com/tong_poems.html>

Tongue twisters can be hard to read.

Dr Seuss was famous for
writing tongue twisters!

1 Read this tongue twister.

Betty Botter had some butter,
'But', she said, 'this butter's bitter.
If I bake this bitter butter,
It would make my batter bitter.
But a bit of better butter,
That would make my batter better'.
So she bought a bit of butter –
Better than her bitter butter –
And she baked it in her batter;
And the batter was not bitter.
So 'twas better Betty Botter
Bought a bit of better butter.

2 Turn all the 'b' words into 'p' words and read it again!

3 Read this.

Larry liked loopy Lucy,
But Lucy liked little lambs.

How quickly can you say it? _____ seconds

4 Write your own tongue twister sentence. Try to use words that begin with the
same letter!

_____

_____

Chant it!

Objective

Recite, write and perform playground chants

Activities covered

- Reading chants as a group
- Practising chants
- Writing a chant as a group
- Performing a chant as a group

Background information

Playground chants require fluency, so the pupils should practise reading them a number of times. Increasing a pupil's self-esteem in reading requires the pupil to be reading something well, so there should be an opportunity where pupils are given reading to practise, so that they can deliver the reading almost flawlessly. Reading given should always be aimed at a pupil's stage of development. Always be supportive and encouraging when pupils are reading. Pupils should never feel afraid to read.

Before the lesson

Prepare examples of other playground chants for the pupils to read. The class will need to be divided into small groups.

The lesson

1. Discuss playground chants with the class.
2. The pupils read and practise the two chants in small groups, adding actions.
3. The pupils write their own chant, using the given format, then perform their chant for the class.
4. As a class, recite common playground chants.

Answers

1.–3. Teacher check

Additional activity

Pupils can:

Practise reading texts such as poems, paragraphs, letters, play parts, parts of class reader, factual information etc.

1 Read these playground chants with a small group. Read them a few times until you have them right, then add actions.

Little bird, little bird, hop about!

Little bird, little bird, do not shout!

Little bird, little bird, sing a song!

Little bird, little bird, what is wrong?

Little bird, little bird, you can't stay?

Little bird, little bird, fly away!

Little girl, little girl, please be neat!

Little girl, little girl, take your seat!

Little girl, little girl, please behave!

Little girl, little girl, don't hit Dave!

Little girl, little girl, do not run!

Little girl, little girl, your work's not done!

2 In your group, write your own chant.

Little _____, little _____, _____

Little _____, little _____, _____

Little _____, little _____, _____

Little _____, little _____, _____

3 Practise your chant with actions, then perform it for the class.

What's he like?

Objective

Respond to characters and events in a poem

Activities covered

- Reading a poem
- Describing a character
- Answering true or false
- Naming and drawing a character from a poem

Background information

When discussing characters, the pupils should be discussing familiar characters, ones they know well. The pupils know characters from TV shows and films, so these could be discussed first. The pupils could talk about positive parts of their own character too!

Before the lesson

The teacher can have examples of characters to discuss with the class.

The lesson

1. The teacher explains to the class what 'character' means.
2. The teacher reads the poem **My brother** with the class.
3. The poem is discussed and the teacher goes through harder words, such as 'gross', 'fibs', 'grubby', 'sardine'.
4. The pupils describe the brother in one word.
5. The pupils answer true or false questions.
6. The pupils give the brother a name and draw a picture of him.

Answers

1. Teacher check
2. grubby/dirty/messy/nasty/bad/hungry etc.
3. (a) F   (b) T   (c) T   (d) F   (e) F
4. Teacher check

Additional activities

Pupils can:

1. Look at and discuss characters in fairytales, other poems, TV shows, cartoons etc.
2. Write about a family member, focusing on positive points only.

Recommended reading:
(characters)
Colin by Allen Ahlberg
Billy McBone by Allen Ahlberg
Please Mrs Butler by Allen Ahlberg
Babysitter by Steve Turner

1 Read this poem.

> ### My brother
>
> My little brother is gross,
> And is never, ever clean!
> He often tells such nasty fibs,
> And can be rather mean.
>
> He plays with stupid, silly toys,
> Like motorbikes and guns,
> He never talks, but rather shouts,
> And never walks, but runs!
>
> His clothes are always grubby,
> His hair in a big mess,
> His fingers are always sticky,
> But he could not care less.
>
> He always seems to be hungry,
> And gobbles his food real quick,
> He loves a sardine sandwich,
> The thought just makes me sick!
>
> He's mad, he's bad, disgusting too,
> But I love him anyway,
> Don't touch a hair upon his head,
> Or I will make you pay!

2 Write one word to describe the brother.

_____

3 Colour true or false.

(a) Her brother hates fish.

☐ true ☐ false

(b) The poet loves her brother.

☐ true ☐ false

(c) Her brother always runs.

☐ true ☐ false

(d) Her brother is very clean.

☐ true ☐ false

(e) Her brother eats slowly.

☐ true ☐ false

4 Give the brother a name.

draw him

How do you feel?

Objective

Express feelings in writing

Activities covered

- Reading a poem
- Answering questions about a poem
- Completing sentences about feelings

Background information

Pupils may find it difficult to identify different feelings, so there should be much class discussion at the beginning of this lesson. Here, the pupils can give examples of how they felt in different situations. They will need to be reminded that they should respect other people's feelings at all times.

Before the lesson

A list of feelings could be prepared to discuss with the class.

The lesson

1. As a class, discuss different feelings and what makes someone sad, happy, excited, bored, jealous, angry, worried etc.
2. Read the poem **Alone** to the class and follow with a discussion on how the poet is feeling.
3. The pupils answer Questions 2 to 4.
4. The pupils complete sentences, stating when they had different feelings.

Answers

1.–5. Teacher check

Additional activities

Pupils can:

1. Write about a happy/sad experience they have had.
2. Bring in a recent photo of themselves and write about how they were feeling at the time.
3. Identify the feelings in various scenarios given by the teacher.
4. Draw themselves and write a sentence about how they are feeling. These can be displayed in the classroom.

Homework suggestion

Ask family members how they are feeling and make note of it to discuss in class the following day.

Recommended reading:

Looking for Dad by Brian Patten

Nightmare by Steve Turner

Fall in love by Fred Sedgwick

1 Read this poem.

> ### Alone
>
> *We were such good friends,*
> *and now we are not.*
> *Did I do something wrong?*
> *Was I nasty, or what?*
>
> *We were always together,*
> *we had such great fun.*
> *Now you have other mates,*
> *and I don't have one.*

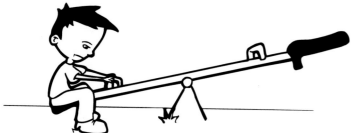

2 Which word describes this poem?

☐ sad ☐ happy

3 Have you ever felt like this?

☐ yes ☐ no

4 What should the poet do?

_____

_____

_____

_____

5 Finish these sentences.

(a) I am sad when

_____

(b) I am happy when

_____

(c) I am excited when

_____

(d) I am angry when

_____

(e) I am scared when

_____

> Never make fun of
> other people's feelings!

Write about it!

Teachers notes

Objective

Write about experiences to create a diamante poem

Activities covered

- Talking about experiences
- Reading a diamante poem
- Writing a diamante poem
- Reading a poem to class
- Assessing a poem

Background information

Pupils are usually eager to talk about their own experiences and the lesson should start with a general discussion about experiences they may have had. These experiences can be happy, sad, terrifying, sad, exciting etc. They should also be reminded to listen carefully to other pupils' experiences during the discussion. In this lesson, the pupils write about their experience in the form of a poem so they will have to capture the essence with only a few words. Give the pupils a few silent minutes to think about their experience before they begin the writing task.

Format for diamante poem:

Noun

2 adjectives

3 participles

4 nouns

3 participles

2 adjectives

1 noun

Before the lesson

Collect examples of material to read which looks at the experiences of others.

The lesson

1. Read to the class poems/parts of stories etc. that tell of people's experiences.
2. Read the diamante poem *The sea* and discuss it.
3. Explain how to write a diamante poem. An example could be done together as a class using an imaginary experience. Point out how the poem is a diamond shape at the end. The pupils should write in the middle of the lines provided, and can do it in light pencil first to get the shape right. All words that the pupils write must have something to do with their experience.
4. The pupils are given a few minutes to quietly think about the experience they are going to write about before they write their own diamante poem.
5. The pupils read their poems out to the class.
6. The pupils assess their poem.

Answers

1.–5. Teacher check

Additional activity

Pupils can:

Write about experiences in the form of a story, letter, news article, diary, poem etc.

(134) **Poetry skills**   Prim-Ed Publishing® ~ www.prim-ed.com

Think of something that has happened to you.

Can you see this poem is a diamond shape?

1 Read the poem about this experience.

The sea

The sea

Angry, moody

Crashing, splashing, crushing

Waves, sandbank, salt water, beach

Pounding, drowning, sinking

Scary, rough

Ocean

2 What do you think happened to the poet?

_____

3 Write a poem about something that has happened to you. Using the pattern below.

Write in the middle of the lines.

Title _____

1 naming word _____

2 describing words _____

3 **ing** words _____

4 naming words _____

3 **ing** words _____

2 describing words _____

1 naming word _____

4 Read your poem to the class.

5 Give your poem a score out of 10. ☐

Sense it!

Objective

Draw and write about sensory experiences

Activities covered

- Discussing senses
- Writing a poem

Background information

This lesson focuses on describing a holiday using all the senses. Begin the lesson by discussing the five senses to remind the pupils what they are.

Before the lesson

Prepare pictures of the five senses.

The lesson

1. Discuss the five senses with the pupils. They give examples of things they can taste, smell, see, hear and touch.
2. Read the poem as a class, discussing which lines are about seeing, hearing, smelling etc.
3. The pupils choose a holiday they enjoy (Christmas, Halloween, Easter, St Patrick's Day etc.).
4. The pupils brainstorm the topic to list holiday words associated with each sense.
5. Go through the format of the poem with the pupils.
6. The pupils write their own poem.
7. The pupils can then draw a large face and hand on an A3-sized sheet of paper. They can take each line and write it in the shape on the face; e.g. The line about 'seeing' they can write in the shape of the eye, the line about 'hearing', they write in the shape of the ear, the line about 'touch' they write in the shape of a hand and so on. It is easier if the pupils draw all the outlines with a pencil first, as big as possible, and then write the words over their drawing. The poems can then be displayed.

Answers

1.–4. Teacher check

Additional activities

Pupils can:

1. Describe objects using all the senses.
2. Write about what they see/smell/taste/touch/hear in a particular place. Others must guess what they are thinking of.
3. Write about how feelings might be described using the senses; e.g. If sadness was a colour it would be...., If sadness was a sound it would be...... etc.

Homework suggestion

Describe an object at home, using all the senses.

We have five senses – sight, hearing, smell, taste and touch.

Christmas can tickle all your senses!

1 Read the poem.

Christmas

A tall, sparkling Christmas tree,

Turkey sizzling in the oven,

Jingle Bells! Jingle Bells!

Roasted chestnuts, piping hot,

A gift with my name on it,

Christmas

I don't care who you are, get those reindeer off my roof!

2 Write the name of a holiday that you enjoy. _____

3 Write a poem about it and your senses.

There are four basic tastes: sweet, salty, sour and bitter.

Line 1: Name of holiday   _____

Line 2: Something you see   _____

Line 3: Something you smell   _____

Line 4: Something you hear   _____

Line 5: Something you taste   _____

Line 6: Something you touch   _____

Line 7: Name of holiday   _____

4 Follow your teacher's instructions for drawing a display of your poem.

I remember

Objective

Write and draw about memories

Activities covered

- Reading a memory poem
- Talking about memories
- Writing a memory poem
- Drawing a picture

Background information

For this lesson, pupils are talking and writing about memories. Explain that they must think back as far as they can. There should be much discussion at the beginning of the lesson, with the pupils explaining any memories they have of their early childhood.

Before the lesson

The pupils can bring in an old photo of themselves or anything else that sparks a memory.

The lesson

1. Read the poem as a class.
2. Discuss with the pupils the memories this boy has.
3. The pupils can talk in general about memories they have, thinking back as far as they can.
4. The pupils write a poem, starting their lines with 'I remember ...' The poem does not have to rhyme.
5. The pupils draw a picture of one of their memories.

Answers

1.– 3. Teacher check

Additional activities

Pupils can:

1. Write stories and poems about topics from other subjects.
2. Write a story with the inclusion of a comic strip.
3. Write exaggerated stories and poems.
4. Write class/group stories.
5. Write different forms of poetry.

Websites:

(for teachers)

<www.poetryteachers.com>

<www.poetryzone.ndirect.co.uk>

<http://42explore.com/poetry.htm>

1 Read the poem about this boy's memories.

I remember the tablecloth, with the tiny purple flowers,
I remember the old radio, and listening for hours,
I remember the house next door, it had a set of swings,
I remember my Postman Pat blanket, and the comfort that it brings,
I remember the corner shop, with its ice-creams and treats,
I remember the summer holidays, kids playing in the streets,
I remember the Market Square, where the fountain stood,
I'm glad I can remember, these memories are good!

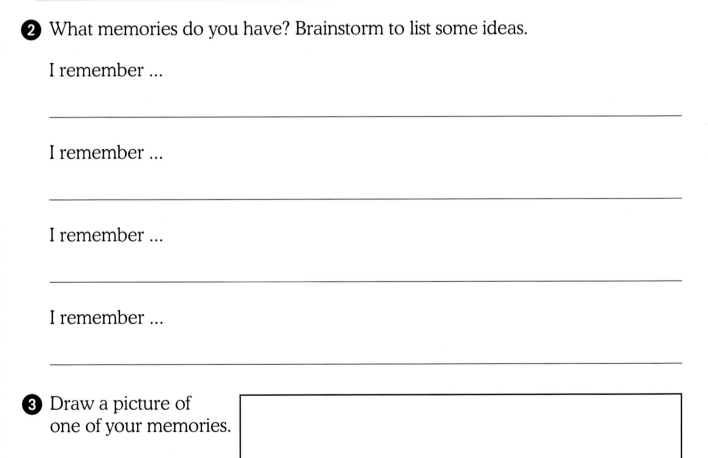

2 What memories do you have? Brainstorm to list some ideas.

I remember ...

_____

I remember ...

_____

I remember ...

_____

I remember ...

_____

3 Draw a picture of one of your memories.

Posh Josh

Objective

Express likes and dislikes about events and characters in poems

Activities covered

- Reading a poem
- Discussing a character
- Writing about a character

Background information

Although the poem is about a generally unlikeable character, the pupils will need to be reminded that having lots of money doesn't make a person nasty – it is the boy's attitude towards others that makes him difficult to get along with. When discussing characters, teachers could remind pupils that although some people may be nasty/moody etc. everyone also has good qualities and nobody is perfect.

Before the lesson

Collect other examples of poems about different characters.

The lesson

1. Read the poem **Posh Josh** as a class.
2. The poem is discussed, focussing on the character of Josh.
3. The pupils answer questions about Josh's character.
4. The pupils choose a character. This should be a fictional character from a book/TV show/film/comic/cartoon etc.
5. The pupils write four sentences about their chosen character. These should be full sentences.

Answers

1.–5. Teacher check

Additional activities

Pupils can:

1. Read other poems about characters; e.g. **Gentle, sweet and deadly** by Clive Webster, **Sir's a secret agent** by Tony Langham, **High flyers** by Brian Moses, **Out of season** by Paul Cookson, **Playing tennis with Justin** by David Harmer.
2. Write a character sketch on a given character.
3. Write a character sketch on themselves, focusing on the positive points only.
4. Write a simple clerihew about a character:

   4 lines long

   1st line/2nd line rhyme

   1st line has the name of the character

   3rd line/4th line rhyme

   The poem should be humorous, and can be any rhythm.

1 Read the poem about a boy called Josh.

'Posh' is a slang word meaning 'classy' or 'superior'.

There's a boy in my class called Josh,
He's rich and oh, so posh!

He goes everywhere in a limousine,
And often has dinner with the queen!

He will not share his thousands of toys,
He says we are poor, rough boys!

Each week his dad gives him fifteen grand,
But he won't even sponsor our school band!

He won't play with us, he calls us 'trash',
He says you're nothing if you don't have cash.

At lunchtime, his chefs bring a special hot meal,
(And not a sandwiches-and-water deal!)

He walks around with his nose in the air,
While his butler follows him everywhere!

Now people might say we're a jealous lot,
But I'd rather have friends, than what he's got!

2 Write what you think of Josh. I think ...

_____

_____

_____

_____

_____

3 Write one thing you would say to Josh.

_____

_____

_____

_____

4 Choose a character you know from a book, TV show, film or cartoon.

5 Write four sentences about this character.

_____

_____

_____

_____

Listen to the music

Objective

Listen to music and write about it

Activities covered

- Reading an example of a poem
- Listening to music
- Responding to music
- Writing a poem

Background information

For this lesson, choose music that is likely to evoke strong feelings in the pupils. Some classical music would be suitable – perhaps something powerful or strong. When the pupils are listening to the music they must close their eyes and concentrate. Tell the pupils beforehand what task they are going to do so that they are aware of what is expected of them and they can think while the music is playing.

Before the lesson

Prepare samples of music to play for the pupils.

The lesson

1. Explain to the pupils that they will be listening to music to help them write a poem.
2. Read the poem as a class.
3. Play a piece of music while the pupils close their eyes and listen. No discussion takes place at this time.
4. The pupils list words to describe the music; e.g. 'loud', 'fast', 'scary'.
5. The pupils write a poem of their own, following the format of the example in Question 1. The music can continue to play while the pupils are writing.
6. The pupils write the title of the piece of music they listened to.
7. Some pupils can read out their poem to the class, while the music is playing, and the music can be discussed.
8. The pupils can rewrite their poem, decorate it and display it.

Answers

1.–5. Teacher check

Additional activities

Pupils can:

1. Write a story while listening to music and then read it out while the music is playing.
2. Listen to music and draw a picture depicting the music. Different types of music could be played and the pupils could compare their pictures.
3. Listen to music that tells a story; e.g. ***Peter and the wolf*** by Prokofiev or ***The four seasons*** by Vivaldi.
4. Listen to various different types of music and draft a writing piece inspired by the music.

1 Read the poem.

> *The rough sea,*
> *waves bashing the sand,*
> *on a cold, winter's day,*
> *on a pebble beach,*
> *at high tide.*

Mozart started composing music when he was four years old!

2 Close your eyes and listen to a piece of music.

3 Write a poem using the music and the pattern below.

Line 1: What does the music make you think of?

_____

Line 2: What action is happening?

_____

Line 3: When does it happen? (time)

_____

Line 4: Where does it happen?

_____

Line 5: Why is it happening?

_____

4 What music did you listen to? _____

5 Read your poem to the class.